PRAISE FOR EX~~PEDITION SCIENCE~~

Part fearless cave-exploring field researcher and part P. T. Barnum, with all the panache of a pro wrestling promoter, Becky Schnekser is every bit the science teacher that Ms. Frizzle aspired to be: colorful, vibrant, and larger-than-life. Brimming with ideas and busting with heart and humor on each page, *Expedition Science* is packed with all kinds of strategies to help teachers rekindle their passion and learn how to create classrooms that bring life, joy, and relevance back to a world of all-too-stodgy science classrooms. In a word? It's magic.

> —**John Meehan,** author of *EDrenaline Rush*

Expedition Science is the science book I've been waiting for my entire career. Becky makes science fun, she makes it important, her ideas make it engaging, and maybe most of all, Becky makes it doable for any teacher. Becky has been all over the world with National Geographic and knows how to teach kids and other teachers how to be science fanatics as well.

> —**Adam Welcome,** author of *Teachers Deserve It*

Now more than ever, it's important to foster a love of learning science in students from a young age, and *Expedition Science* is a catalyst for that. After reading just the first chapter, I was excited to get back inside my own classroom the next day and start brainstorming ideas with my students. The examples Becky presents, the connections she makes, and the resources she provides are practical and easy to implement for educators at all levels.

> —**Becky Thal,** fifth-grade math/science teacher and educational consultant

If you were to close your eyes and imagine the perfect learning environment for your children, Becky's class is what you'd envision. *Expedition Science* is the book that will help you to be the teacher you've always dreamed of being. It is a perfect mix of student-focused learning and engagement, practical pedagogy, and that sprinkle of magic that makes kids want to go to school.

—**CJ Reynolds,** author of *Teach Your Class Off*

From expeditions across foreign lands to using Hot Wheels and VSCO girl personalities, educators everywhere are called to inspire discovery within the minds of our students. In this amazing book, Becky Schnekser not only shares why this is so vital but how it can be accomplished today, in your school, in your classroom, for your kids. I strongly encourage you to sit down, settle in, and get ready for an amazing educational expedition.

—**Dave Schmittou,** author and full professor of educational leadership

Expedition Science is not just for science educators! This book is packed with teaching anecdotes and tips for educators looking to get their students ready for exploration. Becky Schnekser's passion for teaching shines through on every page. She skillfully offers practical ideas on how to connect science to the various disciplines we teach. She shows the importance of making learning an experience.

—**Kevin Butler (@thekevinjbutler),** elementary school teacher and director of curriculum and instruction

Becky Schnekser shares the personal journey that brought her to a deep love of science and science education, and her actual journeys to some of the most amazing places on earth, and connects these to the learning journey our students go through. *Expedition Science* is both a blueprint for creating powerful science classrooms (whether they're inside walls or not) and an inspiration for all content-area teachers. Now, get out there and explore!

—**Denis Sheeran (@MathDenisNJ),** author *of Instant Relevance*

Becky enthusiastically invites us all into her various "classrooms" and highlights in the most accessible way how important it is to bring science to life. Topics and strategies often discussed abstractly at professional development conferences and teacher trainings are made meaningful through real, messy, wonderful examples. Becky helps us imagine ourselves alongside her and her students as we go on multiple expeditions together. Just like her students, we are transformed into explorers and scientists. Reading *Expedition Science* will fill you with joy, hope, and plenty of inspiration.

—**Dan Kinzer,** founder and guide at Pacific Blue Studios, National Geographic Grosvenor Teacher Fellow

Expedition Science beautifully captures what science education should be: experiences, discovery, inquiry *and* a love for the environment! Through the power of storytelling and flexible/ mindful teaching, Becky Schnekser hits a home run her first time out. I look forward to her future contributions in this evolving but often overlooked space in education.

—**Jorge Valenzuela,** education coach, author, and advocate

Expedition Schnekser is a map for innovation, engagement, and passion for science education. Readers will be inspired to explore and inquire thanks to Schnekser's brisk and upbeat writing style. Keep this book at the top of your bookshelf!

—**Sean Gaillard,** author of *The Pepper Effect*, podcaster, and principal

After growing up as a science nut, always wanting to blow stuff up or find how things worked, reacted, or moved, I became a science major in college. The focus of science stayed with me as an educator, always trying to bring the real world of exploration into my classrooms. Becky is the science teacher I wish I had. This book welcomes the reader to live vicariously through Becky's lens of science mania. Science is so much more than the world sees.

—**Jeff Kubiak,** antiracist educator and
author of *One Drop of Kindness*

EXPEDITION SCIENCE

EXPEDITION SCIENCE

SCIENCE

EMPOWERING LEARNERS THROUGH EXPLORATION

BECKY
SCHNEKSER

Expedition Science: Empowering Learners through Exploration
© 2021 Becky Schnekser

This book is available at special discounts when purchased in quantity for educational purposes or for use as premiums, promotions, or fundraisers. For inquiries and details, contact the publisher at books@daveburgessconsulting.com.

Published by Dave Burgess Consulting, Inc.
San Diego, CA
DaveBurgessConsulting.com
Library of Congress Control Number: 2021933685
Paperback ISBN: 978-1-951600-82-2
E-book ISBN: 978-1-951600-83-9

Cover illustration by Diana Stoyanova
Cover and interior design by Liz Schreiter
Editing and production by Reading List Editorial: readinglisteditorial.com

To all of the young explorers who at
some point in time are told, far too soon,
that they can't be or do something . . .

To everyone who lost their curiosity and
love for science far too early . . .

To all of the educators who
push boundaries . . .

To anyone described as a nerd (as if it's
negative) instead of passionate . . .

To my mom, Patricia Winner

CONTENTS

FOREWORD

If Becky had been my science teacher, I know my life would have been very different. I still think I would have ended up in the sciences; however, I can't help but think that her influence would have made my career path a more direct (and enjoyable) journey of exploration, rather than the bitter obstacle course that seemed too eager to weed me out.

I hated science class throughout middle and high school, which may seem strange coming from a professional scientist, NatGeo Explorer, TED main stage speaker, and PhD candidate with over a decade of research experience. In school, method and repetition eclipsed curiosity and exploration, and the natural world's only place seemed limited to that *one* captivating image at the very start of each chapter that's meant to lure you in before assigning more word problems. One high school teacher even told me to never consider a career in science because I was no good at math and would get outcompeted.

The great irony here is that *outside* of school, I was reading every nature book I could find, watching every science show available, and visiting museums every chance I got. I *loved* science, but exclusively outside the classroom. Fortunately, a serendipitous college science elective would help me reconnect and fall in love with academic science—ultimately leading me to make it my career. Still, knowing how close I came to renouncing science forever and missing out on my dream job gives me chills.

Unfortunately, my science class "survivor story" is in no way unique to me. In fact, there are countless professional scientists, educators, science communicators, and students who share a similar experience with science in the classroom. It makes me wonder how many potential Einsteins and Goodalls were weeded out by traditional science education—and that is precisely why Becky's book is so important.

In *Expedition Science*, Becky takes us on a journey of science education that comes across as authentic, informative, disruptive, and—above all—lived. Becky has lived the experience of being a science student, educator, and researcher; in *Expedition Science*, she unites these lived experiences to present us with a solid snapshot of the state of science education. She sheds light on why it is the way it is and, most importantly, provides tools to not only reinvigorate science education but to also use it as a tool for positive global change.

Becky's writing is refreshingly authentic, as if she is having a one-on-one conversation with you, the reader. Moreover, her ability to make things feel positive, even when highlighting challenges, is a part of her personality that shines through in her writing. When the world gets dark, she becomes a light, imparting hope through her own actions and hard work. Most importantly, she tries to inspire the same superpower in her students.

Ultimately, after years of knowing Becky personally and professionally through our work in the field and the classroom, at conferences, and virtually, I consider her one of the most committed, dedicated, and engaged science educators I know. She is always trying to improve and find new ways to get her students excited about education. She is constantly growing in her craft, seeking to improve, and finding creative, often unorthodox ways to teach the "same old science." This makes her very disruptive in an inertia-heavy educational subject.

Her passion for teaching science makes her revelation regarding an early aversion to science teaching in her career all the more shocking. At the start of *Expedition Science*, she shares how she viewed the subject as a "necessary evil." Her honesty reveals how the science class survivor archetype affects teachers just as badly as it does students. But as Becky shows us, we do not have to accept this as the way things will always be.

Ultimately, this book is important because the blunt reality is that the way we teach science, talk about science, or even teach others to teach about science is in desperate need of an overhaul. Science education and the critical thinking, observational, and logical skills that it cultivates have never been more important. As a species we are facing major crises, from the climate, pandemics, and superbugs to mass extinction events and limited resources—and if these problems were not enough on their own, they only become more complicated with the growing voice of antiscience movements. In speaking with many climate change deniers, anti-evolution groups, antivaccination voices, and others, it disturbs me to hear their versions of the science class survivor story. Too often, we don't trust what we don't understand, and especially if there is trauma or accumulated negative experiences, these surface as clear influencers in being antiscience. For anyone paying attention to the state of global affairs, this is serious and directly affects our future.

Expedition Science is a much-needed step in the right direction. Science is just as much about celebrating repeatability as it is about celebrating new discoveries. More importantly, science is a journey, and that is exactly what Becky takes us on. So, let's dig into that! Let's get excited! Let's make it fun! I am very grateful to Becky for writing this book, and I only hope that when my child becomes a middle school student, the science education establishment will have taken more than a few notes from Becky.

—ANDRÉS RUZO CALLEJAS,

National Geographic Explorer, geoscientist, founder and director of the Boiling River Project

INTRODUCTION

FROM RELUCTANT SCIENCE EDUCATOR TO AMAZON EXPLORER

I am going to begin with a huge secret. For the fifteen years I have been teaching to date, I have kept this secret with me, pushed it to the back of my mind, and definitely kept it off of my laboratory tables. Are you ready?

Great! But . . . I'm not sure I'm ready. So, let me start with a story.

Back in 2006, I sat in the main office of Fairfield Elementary awaiting my first teaching interview, hoping I would begin my career as a fifth-grade teacher. I met the principal, Dr. Sophia Stubblefield, and the assistant principal, Stephanie Haus, and began my interview. They asked me questions about classroom management, how I planned to use data in the classroom, how I might approach colleagues who were hesitant or resistant to my ideas, my organizational style, and so on.

Then I handed Dr. Stubblefield and Mrs. Haus my five-inch, three-ring binder teaching portfolio, which they began to flip through. I was fresh out of college, and this binder held lesson plans, assessments, student work, photographs, project samples, personal reflections, and the like for all subjects I had taught in my student teaching placements of second and fourth grade. Dr. Stubblefield and Mrs. Haus were particularly drawn to my science section.

"So, you like teaching science?" one of them asked. They were both nodding at me, seemingly prompting me to say yes.

No, I do not enjoy teaching science. I haven't enjoyed science since third grade when my teacher told me I wasn't good at math or science. I prefer history and social studies because I feel like students do not enjoy them, so I make it a priority to teach them in an interesting way and energize them about it. That's the truth, but I am no dummy. This is an interview; they are nodding at me. That has to mean something, and it's time to tell a little fib. You need this job, dude, I thought to myself.

One of them followed up with, "The teacher you are replacing taught science."

Well, I know what my answer must be now, I thought.

"Yes, it's pretty fun," I replied.

The truth is I wanted nothing to do with teaching science. To me, it was a necessary evil, and I was hoping to avoid it entirely. Maybe you can relate?

But that interview ended up changing my life. A few days later, while on the beach with a friend from college, the call came, and I was offered the job. I was overjoyed to be employed, and after signing my contract, I promptly bought my dream car—OK, realistic dream car—a MINI Cooper.

August 8, 2006. My MINI Cooper "Cloe" and I celebrating my first teaching contract.

In my first year of teaching, I realized what nearly all elementary school teachers know: science is a neglected subject. Sometimes it is purposely neglected by teachers—it's not something they want to teach or feel skilled in—but oftentimes it is neglected out of necessity to cover state-mandated standards that are tested and chosen as indicators of student and teacher success. Usually, it is a combination of these. Reading, writing, and mathematics overshadow all other subjects, for better or worse.

That was certainly the situation I encountered as I began my teaching career. During orientation week, I was given the city's standard curriculum binder, which, judging by the amount of dust and yellowed pages, had been grossly neglected. After digging in and inquiring with colleagues and our library media specialist about the resources listed, I learned that no one used those resources, no one was teaching science the way it should be taught, and some were not teaching science at all. Honestly, *most* were not teaching it at all.

I made the decision then and there that science instruction, or lack thereof, needed to change, and it would begin with me. Interestingly enough, as this thought entered my mind, a colleague entered my room to ask me if I would take on the role of lead science teacher for our school. "Uh, sure," was my response. And with that, my journey to make science "a thing" began.

Now, fifteen years after that fateful interview, I am a National Geographic certified educator and grantee, Grosvenor Teacher Fellow, and president-elect of the Virginia Association of Science Teachers who does fieldwork in the Amazon with the nonprofit Boiling River Project, leads my students on caving expeditions in the classroom, and completes student-led fieldwork on the school grounds. Science thrills me, and I want to share that passion with you, along with ideas on how you can reimagine science education to provide powerful, authentic experiences for your students.

In the sixteen chapters of this book, I want to take you on an expedition with me to my classroom, both indoors and outdoors, to the

Amazon, and even the Galapagos to see what science can look like with your learners. I want you to see that, yes, science *can* be taught and taught well, no matter the age or experience of your learners. I want you to understand and experience the importance of teaching science alongside core subjects, such as reading, writing, and mathematics. They are all stronger together, just like an expedition team on location.

In reading this book, you will be immersed into my experiences in the field completing scientific expeditions as well as in the classroom, which I hope will spark ideas of your own for your learners. I am a strong believer in sharing ideas, plans, and experiences and working together to make the education world, especially science, what it is truly meant to be: experienced, not just tolerated as a standardized part of curricular programs or a set of content strands to be memorized with no personal connection.

Science inspires.

Science saves lives.

Science is real.

Science is fun.

Science is evolutionary and revolutionary.

Science begs for interaction, exploration, investigation, and connection.

Science is active.

Science is happening all around us all of the time.

So what does all of this look like in school? How can you take your science instruction to the next level? How can you inspire learners to investigate the world around them more critically? How can you empower learners through scientific exploration? This book will answer those questions, provide insight into how it works for me and my learners, and inspire you to do the same.

Are you ready for this expedition? Let's go, Explorers, it's time to disrupt the model and make science relevant, engaging, and integral to the lives of learners of all ages.

Field Season 11 in the Peruvian Amazon investigating microbiology.

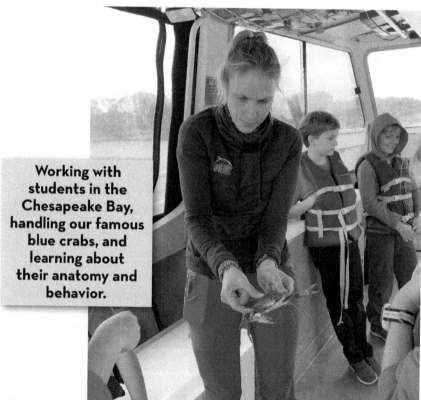

Working with students in the Chesapeake Bay, handling our famous blue crabs, and learning about their anatomy and behavior.

CHAPTER ONE

A VISION FOR SCIENCE EDUCATION

Yesterday it rained, and our garden's rainwater collection ponds, where we complete biodiversity surveys, investigate plants by maintaining them, and explore different methods of irrigation, are now full of rainwater. However, my plan for today in the laboratory is to investigate brook trout anatomy, which is a small piece of our fourth-grade watershed rehabilitation unit. I am ready to talk about external and internal anatomy and draw and label diagrams, carefully broaching the "anal fin" because speaking about anal fins garners giggles, wide eyes, and funny faces from students at the elementary level—or, more likely, students of all ages. I had carefully selected our resources, both print and electronic, provided diagrams ready for labeling and color-coding, curated video content of brook trout for close investigation, and prepared *gyotaku* materials to practice the ancient art of fish printing, which began in Japan as a way to save fishermen from "the one that got away" and "the fish was *this big*" stories.

But as my fourth-grade scientists pour into the laboratory, they immediately begin clamoring, begging, and pleading to go outside. They want to create a fieldwork station and investigate the rainwater collected in the gardens instead of whatever I already have planned for them. It is decision time.

How can I say no?

With a smile on my face, I begin asking them what they will need, what they want to investigate, how they will do it, and finally, whether they are ready to go yet. I have never seen a group of students round up microscopes, test tubes, slides, petri dishes, water sample collection devices, water quality probes, field notebooks, pencils, and lab coats so fast in my life.

This is what it's all about.

We venture out to the garden area, and as a few extremely eager scientists run to grab samples, a few others scream for them to stop; they haven't organized their field station tasks yet. Although they are all ready to jump in, they need to know what they are looking for, have a system for organizing their data and investigation, and decide who will do each task. They eagerly and impatiently set up tables with space to label what they see, where the sample was taken, and all associated data values they feel are necessary to know. They have brought stereoscopes, dissecting microscopes, and compound microscopes because they aren't sure which one will be best for their tasks. They have even thought to bring an extension cord and a power strip.

One scientist uses a microscope in the outdoor field station the class set up to investigate rainwater collection pools.

An entire class of fourth-grade scientists build and use a field station to investigate rainwater pools.

That's commitment.

These are empowered scientists.

This is authentic science.

While they dole out tasks and rotate through different responsibilities, I sit back, take pictures, and observe. They take their own measurements, make their own data collection protocols, organize their data and teams, and only yell for me a few times when they need help identifying what they observe or understanding the observations they have made.

It is organized chaos at its absolute best.

It is authentic fieldwork.

It is student-driven.

It is everything you could possibly hope for as an educator.

Beyond just doing the science, my students also want to share their data with others, especially with scientists we have already connected with in the laboratory. "Can you send a text to Andrés?" they ask. Andrés Ruzo is a geoscientist and National Geographic Explorer I work with each summer, collecting water samples from Shanay-Timpishka, a thermal river system located in the Peruvian Amazon, also known as the Boiling River. My scientists know about that fieldwork and have bonded with Andrés through video sessions throughout the year. Now they want him to see *their* fieldwork. I feverishly send text messages to him with photos of them working.

Three scientists collect rainwater samples to view under a microscope.

Two scientists investigate rainwater samples in petri dishes.

"What about our parents? Can you tell them what we're doing?"

That's easy, too. I have already tweeted to the *world* about their work, and our school's Facebook page will blast the excitement within minutes as well. Later in the afternoon, I will also send an email with details and photographs to their families.

"Can you ask Mr. Mead what these microorganisms are called?"

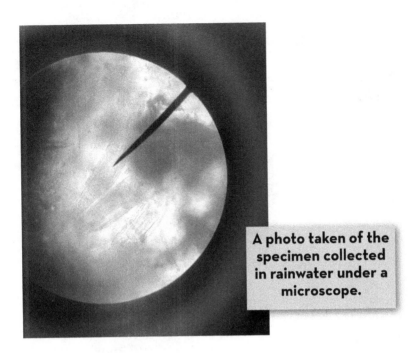

A photo taken of the specimen collected in rainwater under a microscope.

John Mead is a science teacher in Dallas, Texas, who specializes in microbiology and helped us earlier in the year as we investigated water samples with active microorganisms inside. This time, I'm one step ahead of my scientists. I have already messaged John, and he has offered to help us identify our little life-forms!

Amazingly, it's not just my fourth graders who want to investigate the rainwater pools. Both my second-grade class and my third graders ask to as well. What's going on here? Where did they all get this idea? Was there some secret meeting where they told each other what to do and what to say to swindle me into allowing them to complete this task rather than what I had already planned?

No, of course not. The fact of it is, my students are scientists, and this is exactly what scientists do. They seek opportunities for investigation and make it happen. They have been empowered. My job now is to get out of the way and let them get down to work.

EMPOWERING STUDENTS TO BE SCIENTISTS

When we empower our students to be scientists, investigators, questioners, and thinkers, they *do* things. They investigate. They take initiative. They plan. They implement. They surprise you.

A young scientist sets up their fieldwork station with equipment, specimen collection, and sorting containers.

This type of teaching takes time, energy, and commitment—just as all good teaching does. It might not be natural at first. It might be downright difficult. For any number of reasons, you may only be able to incorporate one true field experience per semester for your students. I am not here to tell you it will be easy; what I am here to tell you is that it is worth it in so many ways.

It all begins with a change in thinking, a shift in pedagogy, a complete rewiring of what teaching science looks like. Teaching science should not be about putting a check in a box, which is, unfortunately, what it's become at many schools. Do you know how many elementary classrooms are not even teaching science? Do you know how many middle and high school students have their noses stuck in outdated

A young scientist prepares soil samples to investigate further.

textbooks, which serve as the only or main method of delivering content instruction? Spoiler alert: *all* science textbooks, by the time they
are printed and distributed, are already out of date.

More important, do you know how many *scientists* are using these
methods to learn?

None.

So why, oh why, are we neglecting science and using outdated
instructional methods? It's not OK, and it ends now. No more excuses.
We are going to transform the science classroom, starting at the elementary level and going all the way through high school and beyond.
We owe it to our students and ourselves.

Our classrooms are filled with scientists. In fact, we are all scientists, even if we don't all know it. We explore, discover, try, fail, and
try again. This is literally what science is. By reading this book, you
are practicing science. Maybe you are searching for something (exploration, research, curiosity). Maybe you are trying something new
(experimenting). Maybe this isn't the first thing you have tried (trying

again). If we are natural scientists, especially at a young age, why then do we not see students as scientists? Why do we not see ourselves as scientists? Chances are, somewhere along the line, science was squashed for you. You were turned off for a variety of reasons or in a variety of ways. Your inner scientist died, and that most likely happened in elementary school.

Eight-year-old Becky Winner (now Schnekser) who was told, based on one timed multiplication test in third grade, that she was not good at math and would never be good at science as a result. This is where I lost my love for science.

We want to change this completely. We want our students to thrive in science, enjoy science, and *do* science. How do we do it, though? How do we create and foster that natural curiosity in order to empower future changemakers? Let's begin by considering a few questions.

What if students did real science?

What does it mean to have our students do real science? Real science is not repeating baking soda and vinegar year after year because it looks cool. Don't get me wrong, baking soda and vinegar is a great way to illustrate and familiarize your scientists (yes, scientists) with chemical reactions, but what would be more authentic? Can we use baking soda and vinegar as a jump-off point rather than the entirety of our chemistry labs with students? Can we look at the world around us for chemistry and make it relevant to students? How can we possibly expect anyone to understand scientific concepts if they haven't experienced them? After all, how did you learn to walk? Did you read about it to exhaustion, then were magically able to do it? Did you have someone explain it to you or draw a diagram and off you went, a walking pro? No. You tried some things, you failed frequently, and eventually it worked out for you. How did you learn to read? You tried, you failed a lot, and you eventually mastered it. Our scientists need to do science, not receive it, hear it, or look at it. They need to be fully immersed in science, both in the lab and in the greater world.

Two second-grade scientists find specimens within the grass to collect and study with dissecting microscopes.

What if students collected authentic data?

First, let's ask, what makes data authentic? What kind of data would be useful and relevant? The fact is, all the data students collect in order to answer a question is authentic. The catch is, it all starts with a good question—not a yes/no question, but a question that requires some heavy lifting, investigation, data collection, and critical thinking. Don't get scared here; I know it can sound intimidating when you're first starting out, but I promise you, it all comes together beautifully.

Let's look at some things students can investigate. If you aren't quite ready to allow for open student voice and choice, consider having a few options they can choose from. Perhaps the entire class votes on one of them to investigate together, or you allow different students or groups to investigate different ideas from the list. Either way, this is a great start with authenticity. You can begin incredibly simple. For example, you can ask, "How many times a day does the class sharpen

Two scientists collect data from a trout tank inside the laboratory to ensure water quality values are acceptable to sustain brook trout.

their pencils?" Maybe you put a sheet by the pencil sharpener, where students place a mark each time they sharpen a pencil that day. Maybe you even extend your investigation to what day of the week the class sharpens the most pencils. Just like that, you're jumping into a longitudinal study. That's amazing! Maybe you could even break this data into age of human sharpening their pencil. What age group sharpens the most pencils? On what day do certain age groups sharpen pencils most? Collecting authentic data doesn't require fancy tools. Paper and pencil are proverbial kings in the field, and scientists spend much of their time working with charts, tables, graphs, pictures, drawings, and videos. I know what you're thinking: *Great, but this isn't connected to any content standard I have to teach.* Fear not, there's a lot more we can and will do here.

What if students connected with scientists or even worked side by side or in collaboration with a scientist currently in the field?

"Awesome," I hear you say, but where do you even start? How do you get connected with scientists? Surprisingly, it's not that hard. Scientists know the power of social media and connecting with citizen scientists (anyone who is not a full-fledged scientist but wants to be involved in science), and they want to connect with you. They want to get their message, their passion, and their data out there and have it be used by the public. That exposure is what makes their work relevant, known, and accepted by the world. This is great news for the world of education, where access to resources is often limited. Social media and the internet are ideal for making meaningful and important connections to the world of science, and organizations such as Exploring by the Seat of Your Pants, Explorer Classroom, and Skype a Scientist specialize in connecting classrooms with scientists all over the world and from all disciplines. Other great starting places include nearby state or national parks, local environmental agencies, or even National Geographic. Each region of the United States has a Geographic cohort and coordinator assigned to help involve educators with National Geographic's mission. By the way, have you checked out the online resources and courses available at nationalgeographic.org? If not, you are in for a treat.

Connecting with Scientists

BioBlitz: nationalgeographic.org/projects/bioblitz
BioBlitz events are a way to connect and complete fieldwork along-side scientists. These events bring together community leaders, scientists, students, and others to complete biodiversity surveys in a selected location. These can be held for your school, city, state, or even region. If there is already a BioBlitz event in your area, you can tag along. If not, you can work to create one.

SciStarter: scistarter.org
SciStarter is a collection of citizen and community science proj-ects open for participation whether you are an individual, a group, or a class of students! You and your learners can contribute to a project, helping scientists from around the world collect data!

Additional Resources
- Exploring by the Seat of Your Pants: exploringbytheseat.com
- Explorer Classroom: nationalgeographic.org/education/ student-experiences/explorer-classroom
- Skype a Scientist: skypeascientist.com
- National Parks: nps.gov/teachers/index.htm
- National Geographic: nationalgeographic.org/education/ classroom-resources

What if students studied living scientists?

So often, our students study and, let's be real, memorize facts about scientists who are long gone. Why do we focus so much on dead people? I do not in any way, shape, or form mean that we should ignore them completely; they are historically relevant to the world of science, and we depend on their foundational work. However, there are so many scientists in the field now that we could and should study. When students see that scientists are real, alive, and currently doing big things, they begin to see themselves in the field too, being relevant, important, and integral to the world of science. It's an added bonus if you can connect with those scientists, speak with them, and even help them collect and analyze their data. There is power in the here and now; let's take advantage of the opportunity.

What if students were scientists?

This is where everything leads: to our students being scientists. They will be engaged in the classroom and alive with ideas to investigate. Isn't this what we want for students?

A fifth-grade scientist constructs quadrant for longitudinal soil study using an iPad to document invertebrates found within the quadrant.

Fourth-grade scientists navigate local waterways using nautical maps.

A young scientist poses with a blue crab they collected from the Chesapeake Bay to study ecology and species density locally.

EDUCATOR ASIDE

Dr. Kerryane Monahan (@DrKerryane)
National Board-Certified Teacher, Head of Science

It may sound trite, but science can and does change the world. Science has delivered us life-saving medicines, provided creature comforts to counter nature's challenges, and allowed us to peek into worlds previously beyond our field of vision. Science, as we all learned in school, is a way of knowing and understanding the world around us based on observation, experimentation, data, and evidence. It is a way of thinking and doing, with keystones composed of reason, logic, curiosity, and creativity. The skills and content of science infiltrate every academic discipline, vocation, and job.

Science has a wonderful habit of bringing much joy, discovery, and success to those who participate, but the high moments are often countered with epic and frustrating failures. For every new finding or invention, there is a critical question left unanswered or an experiment that fails to deliver. But that's the thing about science: it isn't designed to satisfy the human mind or provide some sort of reassurance for all of humanity. Science doesn't have the answers; it has the questions. Doing science and thinking scientifically act as a shared language for civilization because science provides a framework for investigating and understanding the natural and physical worlds. Today's Earth needs this common framework now more than ever.

The world's population is nearing 8 billion people, and Earth is feeling the pressure. We need science to meet new healthcare challenges. Emergent diseases will require treatments and vaccines. New and better antibiotics are required to fight evolving bacterial infections. Technologies to meet energy demands, clean water solutions, alternatives to disposable plastics, drought-resistant high-yield crops, accurate weather and storm prediction instrumentation, communications infrastructure, and transportation breakthroughs are just a few areas that require innovation now and into the future to address the consequences of a changing climate and increasing population.

So, the questions we must ask are: Who will these scientific thinkers and doers be? Where will they come from? How will they have the curiosity, passion, and tenacity to take on some of Earth's biggest and most essential challenges?

The answer can be found in science education. We are at a precipice in science education. We can continue to tiptoe along the edge, rehashing the same old pedagogies, or we can take a leap into the abyss and arm the rising generation with the confidence, knowledge, and competency to engage in science to effect positive change in the world. Make no mistake, this doesn't require every student to become a scientist; it only requires that students develop, build, and master critical content and essential skills that underpin innovation. Such empowered students can make an impact through their work, vote, and lifestyle choices. This is no small undertaking. It would require making a break from several powerful entities, including some traditional textbook publishers, organizations that peddle curriculum based on standardized testing, and even some state departments of education that still insist on siloing the academic disciplines. It would require teachers and schools to entirely rethink how we do this whole education thing and upend our desired outcomes and goals.

Until that movement happens, science teachers might ask themselves, "What can I do in my classroom right now to improve science education?" I have some suggestions for you:

1. **Be a scientist.** Every teacher and every student is and must be a scientist. Teachers should consider developing their own research interests and invite students to "join the lab." Envision the university model of a principal investigator (PI) and graduate students, except in the K–12 version. The PI is supportive, open, and interested in student ideas and embeds positive mentorship throughout the research. This will look different depending on your school, location, and grade band. You might be doing advanced research in the lab

or in the field, you could submit for grants, you might write papers for publication, you might participate in community or citizen science projects, or you might connect students with scientists who have expertise in the students' area of interest. The key is that you are actively modeling the work of a scientist while partnering with your students.

2. **Emphasize student research.** I mean both experimentation and exploring the literature. Our students have access to more information than we could've imagined back in the day of searching the card catalog. They must have practice with identifying credible sources, extracting relevant information, using discipline-specific style, and formatting. Students need an abundance of laboratory experience, both recipe- and inquiry-based. Recipe labs model good technique and expose students to a variety of equipment and protocols. Inquiry-based experimentation permits students to practice, modify, apply, and synthesize their learning—literally stretching student brainpower.

3. **Focus on data.** Students at every grade level can collect, interpret, graph, and analyze data. The process of data analysis requires exceptional logic and reasoning skills. In turn, these skills can be applied to other types of thinking and writing across disciplines, leading to better organization and clarity. We all know math gets a bum rap from many students, and that might lie in the theoretical nature of typical math classes. Science is arguably built on a foundation of math, so don't miss the opportunity to reinforce key math concepts in real-world applications. Students might suddenly discover that math is much more interesting.

4. **Join forces.** Don't go at it alone. Partner up with fellow teachers—bonus points if it is a teacher outside of the science department. I teamed up with the geometry teacher to have him teach students how to calculate basal area, tree diameter/height, and acreage of unusual shapes for my environmental science class. Students do research and write papers on endangered species in their world

language classes. During the poetry unit in ninth-grade English, my students create haikus about biomes. One of my absolute favorite partnerships is between the band teacher and physics teachers; they do a unit on sound, and students make their own pan flute from local bamboo. We plan to expand this project to include environmental issues and human geography.

5. **Let go.** You will have to prune your content. You'll need to cover less so students can learn more. This is really tough for teachers to do because everything we've been teaching seems so important. I suggest you focus on the skills you believe students must master, then choose the content that best supports the development of those skills. Some of those skills will be discipline-specific, but so many of them will be beyond any one discipline. Remember your goal: you want to build students who are critical thinkers, creative, tenacious, competent, and empowered to effect positive change in the world. It's probably OK if they don't know the names of the cytochromes of the electron transport chain!

Changing how we teach and learn in science education and focusing on the doing of science and emphasizing scientific thinking while releasing the stranglehold of the content-based curriculum will lead to a generation that embraces science and better understands the role of science in society. We have the power to develop kids who change the world in ways we never imagined but ultimately couldn't imagine any other way.

CHAPTER TWO

START WITH RELEVANCE

grin ear to ear at the boxes of Hot Wheels tracks, connectors, loops, and cars awaiting my fourth-grade engineers' arrival. I can hardly contain my own excitement for what is about to happen.

"What are these?" one of my engineers asks about the large boxes sitting on each table.

"Can we open them?" another chimes in.

"Is this for us?" a third adds.

My engineers read the smile on my face and tear into the boxes with a vengeance. I lean on a stool, arms folded across my chest, face still beaming.

"Oh my gosh! Hot Wheels!"

"I have these at home!"

"Can we make loop-the-loops?"

"What are we doing today?"

My only response is, "Engineers, show me what you can do."

It feels like twenty-one students' birthdays all at once. They tear into materials, yell, throw things, plan, plot, build, test, and decide what cars they like best based on their performance on the track they constructed.

They do science, and they do it on their own. No videos, no paragraphs, no lectures, no directions at all actually. We are natural scientists. Curiosity drives our thirst for knowledge and relevance here is natural—I use a common toy. Some of my students know how to use them; they own the toy. Some have seen or heard of them but have never had the opportunity to explore with them. Others have no experience at all, but they see the items and recognize them as toys—and they all dive in.

I know what you are thinking: *They are learning nothing. What vocabulary are they acquiring? Where are your learning objectives, and what standards are being met? How are you assessing this? Do they know anything about laws of motion? They are just playing.*

Settle down, Sparky. They do experience the content standards, and yes, I assess this. This entire experience is a formative assessment disguised as "just play" that uses relevance, a toy, to engage them from the start.

Do they say potential energy, first law of motion, velocity, inertia, Sir Isaac Newton, friction, or force? No. But they don't need to—yet. They do, however, experience all of the content information.

My next science teacher move is to sneak that content lexicon in there. But already, I have a good understanding of "what they know" and how they interact with these materials. My next moves are going to be to use what they do and what they know and weave in the content vocabulary and concepts.

I will not write the words on a poster, though, and I will not have my scientists copy them down. I will not have them write the words five times tonight for homework in different colors and call it "rainbow words." I will not have questions on a test where they match terms to definitions or cloze passages to insert the words or a spelling or word study test where I call the words and they write them down. I will not even test them on the words.

Engineers explore the use of Hot Wheels tracks.

You read that right. The next interaction they have with these materials, I am going to give them a challenge: find out which car is best at traveling through a track with one loop.

I am also going to limit their materials. Each team will get fifteen tracks, fourteen connectors, one loop and connector piece, and one of each car type. They will be tasked with sketching the track they build, recording their results, and writing a conclusion. They will also have to present to the other teams what they did and how they drew their conclusion.

No, this is not a perfect experimental design system, but I don't care right now. I am teaching force, energy, and motion. As they set off on their challenge, I circulate the room, listening, observing, and coaching if necessary. During this whole section, I am inserting vocabulary as they work. I will catch a team holding the car at the top of a track, ready to drop it, and say, "Wow, that's the location of potential energy. It's stored there just waiting for the car to burst into motion." I find a way to do this with all of the teams multiple times. I do not ask them to repeat "potential energy"; I am just mentioning it and waiting for it to appear naturally in their conversations as engineers. The real test is their explanation time. Who is going to use the words they heard?

FINDING RELEVANCE FOR YOUR LEARNERS

Always—and I cannot stress this enough—start with relevance when planning. Ask yourself why what you are about to experience with your students is *relevant to them* as students, humans, and future change-makers. Take note here that I said "experience," not "teach," and I used the word *with*.

Relevance is what is needed for anyone to "buy into" a situation. *Why and what's in it for me?* Science is not a bitter food that simply has to be ingested; it's fun, it's natural, and it's part of everyday life. We practice science all of the time. Why should it be any different in your classroom?

Don't tell me it's because you have standards to teach; that's a cop-out, an excuse. Those standards are the big-picture outline; how you color within, around, and outside of the lines of that picture is up to you. I propose we color with the best tones, highlights, and eco-friendly glitter sparkles available. Let's make science fun (and relevant) again.

So, you have to teach the laws of motion. Could you rely on videos, lectures, paragraphs, and examples of how Sir Isaac Newton realized these laws? Yep. Do a lot of teachers do this? Sure do. Is it fun? Nope. Is it relevant to your students' lives? Nope. So why are we teaching this way? It's easy. It's how we were taught. We know we are covering the standard this way. . . . The list goes on.

We cannot box ourselves into the *easy way*, the way we have taught something for years, because we already have a folder (electronic or physical) of resources. We must search for relevance today. How is this content experienced in our lives? How can we tap into that to engage our learners? Relevance can be turning your classroom into a Hot Wheels playground, but it doesn't have to be. It can be a simple change in the way you introduce, reinforce, or assess.

Relevance looks, feels, and is experienced differently depending on the concept at hand and your learners. What will engage your learners in something happening now? How are they already spending their time? What is *relevant* in their lives that you can tap into, making your content standards come alive?

In today's world, resources abound, so there is no excuse for sticking with a twenty-year-old or even a one-year-old archive of what you have taught previously if it is no longer relevant in this exact moment. If you need help with ideas, John Meehan has an entire book about gamification called *EDrenaline Rush* that is filled with instant relevance. Additionally, if you connect with him on Twitter, he shares his materials for *free*. Say what?

Books that are great references to help build and connect relevance between your content and the lives and experiences of your learners:

- *Instant Relevance* by Denis Sheeran: I love this book because it provides practical advice you can use tomorrow, or even today, to insert relevance into your classroom practices.

- *Unpack Your Impact* by Naomi O'Brien and LaNesha Tabb: This book follows two incredible educators as they transform their teaching practices and content to be culturally relevant and honest.

- *Teach Your Class Off* by CJ Reynolds: CJ brings you on his journey with students, connecting to their lives and giving you the "real rap" about education from his perspective.

Do we always have to revamp for relevance? Yes . . . and no. I challenge you to evaluate what you are doing year to year, day to day, even class to class, to make sure it is still relevant. You might find that the experience you planned and implemented last year *is* still relevant, but you might find it's not and you have a little work to do. What matters is that you are investing the time to find out.

Does this sound like a lot of work and effort? Good, because it is. But your learners are worth that time and effort. Dedicating yourself to ensuring what you are doing is relevant to them is necessary to be an effective, engaging, and impactful educator.

To be relevant, you need to tune in to your learners' interests, which means you have to know them as human beings. What do they do? How are they spending their time? What are they talking about? What are they *not* talking about? Spend time asking your learners about their interests, checking them out, and maybe even participating in them. Not sure where to start in finding your students' interests? Listen up! What are they talking about? Is it music, a specific dance move, a video game, a smartphone app, a celebrity, a show on a streaming app?

For me, the importance of relevance was driven home the day my fifth graders' extreme wrestler video project became a VSCO girl knockoff. While my students were learning about human body systems, we decided to create overly dramatic wrestler personas that have a special signature move tied to a specific muscle of the human body. We then used a green screen background to film the videos. As I watched a group of girls filming their piece, I realized quickly I had missed the mark in crafting this project. Professional wrestlers were not relevant to these three young ladies; however, VSCO girls were. If you, like I was, aren't familiar with this tween and teen trend that emerged in 2019, I challenge you to google "VSCO girl" then come back. In short, VSCO girls are equivalent to hipster teenagers whose signature quotes are "Save the sea turtles," "sksksksksksks," and ". . . and I oop—" The three girls in this group were more interested in adding these signature lines from VSCO girl videos than becoming WWE-type wrestlers. To their credit, they did their best to apply VSCO touches to professional wrestler personas, but mostly, their video was a VSCO girl video knockoff. Because I was afraid they were not taking the project seriously or perhaps did not understand the requirements, I decided to have a small group conference. I pulled typical teacher moves: "So, tell me about your project." "How is it going?" "What muscle group have you decided to highlight?"

That's when I was quickly brought up to speed on VSCO girls. I learned all about this aspect of their social media life, which made me realize quickly that I had failed to be relevant for them, even if the initial project was spot on, relevant, and engaging for the other five groups in my class. Of course, I could have forced this group to fall in line with the initial project, but who would have benefitted from that dictatorial stance? For this group of young scientists, the project would have been just another thing they were told to do, nothing more. While talking about their VSCO world, we decided together to amend the project. They would use VSCO girl personas to talk about muscles, incorporating those signature quotes while displaying their muscle group knowledge. Voila! They were sold, and they were able to weave the muscular system into a video that better represented their creativity and was a lot more relevant to their lives than my initial project. By tweaking for relevance, they connected with the content better. That's what we want as educators, right?

Relevance matters. What your learners enjoy and spend time doing, viewing, creating, or imitating matters. Get in touch, get involved, and find relevance for all learners, even if it means slightly different constraints, themes, or modifications to assignments to meet your learners where they are. In the end, they will form deeper connections with the content and be proud of what they create, and your relationship will be strengthened.

EDUCATOR ASIDE

John Mead (@Evo_Explorer)

Eugene McDermott Master Teacher of Science, president of Texas Association of Biology Teachers, National Center for Science Education Teacher Ambassador

As a biology teacher who has taught for the past thirty years, I have had the chance to learn about the power of relevant teaching as I have matured. In the early years of my teaching, I assumed my passion for biology was enough to carry the day. If I found something fascinating, of course my students would jump aboard as well. Soon, however, I learned that my passion might be enough to keep interest for a class period, but I needed more than that if I wanted my young biologists to take the topic home and dig deeper.

In my initial years of teaching, my students (like most young scientists) loved microscope work. Two labs were of particular interest: seeing their own cheek cells under the microscope and getting introduced to the alien world of single-celled protozoa. After I had several parents tell me stories of dinner table conversations where their middle schoolers were still abuzz about the mysteries of exploring pond water, a switch flipped in my brain. I was inspired to develop a unit that allowed my students to become explorers as well as resident experts in a field that none of their parents were likely to know anything about other than the names *Amoeba* or *Paramecium*.

Those early experiences with pond water samples led me to realize that samples from our local ponds, streams, and puddles had a surprising diversity of unicellular protists as well as plant fragments and insect larvae. I saw that exploring these samples was much like going on an African safari; with some basic background knowledge, you knew what species you *might* see, but there was no guarantee that you *would* see any particular species on a given game drive. This led me to devise what I now call Microsafaris.

Our Microsafari unit follows a unit on the basics of cell anatomy and physiology, then introduces students to the diversity of cell types found in the six kingdoms of life. This gives young students a baseline from which they can connect with over a dozen species in the first part of the unit. My students would tell you that I repeatedly tell them I am not interested in them memorizing stuff; rather, I want them to learn and connect information into a meaningful tapestry of understanding. This attitude stems from Louis Pasteur's 1854 statement that "Chance favors the mind that is prepared." Memorizing lists of information or data is one of the least inspiring tasks in all of education, but making actual connections between things you've been exposed to is powerful because it promotes the sense that what you're learning is valuable. When your own lightbulb goes off in a moment of discovery, it lights the way forward with a clarity not produced by the feeble flicker of memorization.

Building on the analogy of an actual safari, I introduce students to a collection of creatures that I purchase from a biological supply house. In class, we observe a dozen or so species much in the same way I might take them on a field trip to a zoo to introduce them to African animals. I select samples that provide a range of species that corresponds to what I know my students are likely to see when they actually go on safari. This initial lab work allows them to connect the work from our cell unit to living, active specimens. They can relate their study of organelles like cilia, flagella, and vacuoles to the actual behaviors of cells under their microscope.

This alone is a powerful experience, as middle schoolers get to go home and regale their families with tales of "glass spiky balls," "giant pink cannibal cells," "microscopic trumpeters," and "aquatic wolfpacks." In addition to having a "cool" classroom experience, students come back to class with a sense of being an expert in something that none of their parents or family members know anything about. While I love how this helps build a sense of scientific self-confidence in my young student scientists, the lesson does not end there.

Once they have this knowledge of these microscopic creatures, it's time to move on to applying their newfound expertise. We start to collect samples of local pond, stream, and puddle water to cultivate several classroom containers that we refer to as our "pond water zoos." While the biodiversity of these cultured samples will not precisely match the dozen species we studied before, my "micronauts" are primed to see new species that fit into the same broad classification groups as some of the species they do know. This inevitably leads them to provided field guides that expand their understanding. They also take great pleasure in helping each other ID new species and share what they have seen from their sample of the day. These interactions provoke great discussions about species interactions, the nature of the microecosystems in the containers, and inevitably the desire of students to get back out in nature to collect new samples.

Over the years, as technology has improved, we've also gained the ability to record our adventures under the microscopes. This ability has students taking microscope videos they record on cell phones or with microscope-mounted cameras and sharing them (and their expertise and hypotheses) with family and friends beyond the classroom. Indeed, the ability to share widely (through my YouTube channel: youtube.com/user/jsmead) has led to conversations and feedback from all over the world. Talk about the feeling of value and relevance when students hear that their peers, as well as adults interested in the micro worlds, have seen and interacted with their work!

A wonderful surprise grew out of this project several years ago when I received a call from National Geographic explorer Andrés Ruzo. Andrés is well known for being the first Western scientist to explore the amazing Boiling River (locally called Shanay-Timpishka or "boiled by the heat of the sun") in the Peruvian Amazon. One of my former sixth graders joined Andrés's team as a high schooler and helped design and build equipment to function in the almost boiling waters of the Shanay-Timpishka. Andrés came to our school to talk with me and another teacher about how he might work to help provide greater opportunities for this student, given that he had shown such great promise with his engineering and photography skills. During that visit, as I toured Andrés around our science building, I showed him our pond water zoo containers. That led to an invitation to join the Boiling River team for the summer of 2019 to serve as the lead microscopist for the MicroAmazon project. The MicroAmazon team focused on sampling various sections of the river, then looking at those samples upon our return to basecamp.

Upon running my Microsafari experience with my students this past year, we not only had all the benefits of our previous explorations, but my Boiling River stories encouraged students to actively question how extremophile microbes and insects might have evolved. Upon appreciating the connection between this very small, isolated ecosystem and the work they had done in class, they also became aware of and interested in how such a small area could very much be impacted by climate change. From something that starts as a fun and engaging basic microscope lab, young scientists are now engaged in questions that "real" scientists are wrestling with. These students wind up going home and having questions and conversations not just about *Amoeba* or *Stentor*, but about their place in microecosystems and how the choices a twelve-year-old in Texas makes might impact rare extremophiles in the Peruvian Amazon, questions I would fervently argue are *far* more valuable than memorized factoids for a standardized test.

The value of a teacher doing this sort of fieldwork is threefold. First, it connects the Microsafari project to a much bigger global project that uses the same set of tools and techniques that my middle schoolers are using in our Microsafari lab. This promotes the feeling that even preteens can do "real" science and that the development of observational and analytical skills is relevant and not just "busy work" to be done for a grade.

Second, when students see their teacher in the field participating in exploration and research, it casts that teacher in the role not only of "teacher" but also of "scientist." Such a perception makes science a field those students are more likely to follow. A 2017 study of American attitudes toward science showed that only 19 percent of respondents could name an "actual living scientist," which demonstrates that our adult population never developed a deep understanding regarding the workings of science.[1] I was pleasantly surprised when I polled my students this past year with the same question, and more than half of my students listed *me* as a living scientist. When students see their teachers as experts in a field, it makes the whole science experience much more accessible and relevant for them. Students who view science as a welcoming endeavor better understand the nature of science. They comprehend that science is not merely a collection of facts and answers, but rather an ongoing process that arrives at reliable conclusions, thanks to skills of observation, hypothesis-making, and rigorous analysis. In a world that is ripe with science denialism, we need a new generation of students who understand that the process of doing science is more consequential than some mere memorization of facts to be recalled for the goal of a score on a high-stakes standardized test.

Finally, when students have teachers and mentors who are experienced in "doing science," they also learn that good science is often the result of being able to weave together questions, observations, and related threads of background knowledge to arrive at an understanding that is richer, deeper, and more relevant than a simple bullet point on a Google slide.

When teachers of any subject provide their students with this sort of framework for learning, their students become so much more than collectors of factual fragments. They become thinkers who can weave beautiful tapestries of understanding. And a skill such as intellectual weaving leads to lifelong learners who become adept at seeing and creating connections as they mature through their academic lives. If we do our jobs as teachers, hopefully that's the end result we all are able to produce.

---

1 researchamerica.org/news-events/81-percent-americans-can%E2%80%99t
-name-single-living-scientist

CHAPTER THREE

IT'S AN EXPERIENCE, NOT A LESSON

"**E**xplorers," I say in a dramatic voice as I greet my third-grade scientists outside of my darkened, blocked classroom, "I just found a cave system that's been unexplored, never entered by humans, much less by experienced scientists like you all."

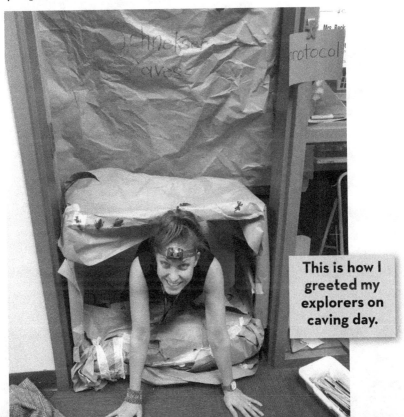

This is how I greeted my explorers on caving day.

Gasps, smiles, laughter, and whispers fill the hallway as they realize why I have been wearing a headlamp all day and why I have been asking them all week to bring in flashlights, lanterns, and headlamps for Friday.

"Wait. Are we going in caves?" one scientist asks.

"Is it safe?" asks another.

"How do we even know what to do?" asks a third scientist.

"We've been asked to enter this cave system and complete a survey. We need to find out exactly what is inside. I've gathered your notebooks and pencils so we can document what we see and experience. We will need to be organized because we are going to be sending our data to a different team of scientists who are tracking all caves in Virginia. Are you ready?"

"But wait! How do we do this?" a scientist yells, his eyebrows curved like Dwayne Johnson.

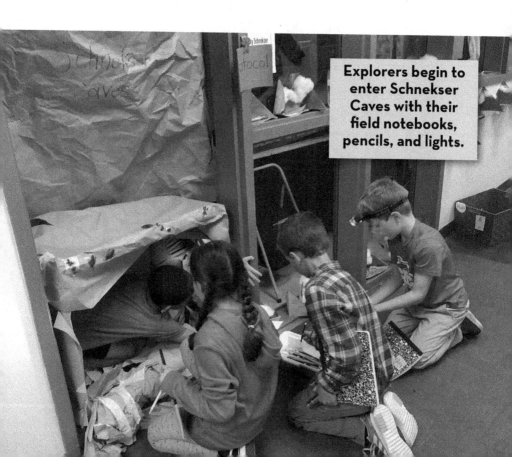

Explorers begin to enter Schnekser Caves with their field notebooks, pencils, and lights.

"These have been undocumented, never studied before. We need to write down everything we see, living and nonliving. We also need to know which cave each thing is found in, how many of each there are, and any information you think this other team might need to know. Also, keep in mind, we do not know if the things we find are dangerous, so we should not touch anything, but just count, record, and draw if you would like."

Teams of scientists pounce on the notebooks and pencils and crawl their way through the entryway of the cave system. Inside, they find a darkened room with five different caves to explore. To enter the system and each cave, they literally have to crawl on their hands and knees, and so do I. Each cave has a name written above it and a different set of life within it to document. To populate the caves, I have used actual data from a study completed by the University of Georgia in which they were tracking sick and infected bats within local cave systems.

"Whoooooooooooa," a group of scientists yell from inside Lear Cave, named after my friend and bat conservationist, Dr. Kristen Lear. I suspect they have found a collection of bats and tarantulas within the cave. Nearly at the same time, I hear screeches of delight and surprise as scientists occupy each of the caves and happen upon other creatures that seemingly appear out of nowhere. That's *exactly* what it is like in the field, especially if you work in locations or times of day or night with very little to no light.

This is it, I think to myself as I take in the scene. Just then another group of scientists call out to me, "Mrs. Schnekser, can you come in Beatles Cave? We want to show you something."

This cave is named in honor of my dear friend Sean Gaillard, author of *The Pepper Effect*. As I crawl into Beatles Cave, the scientists inside are frozen with their only light shining on a large bat "flying" in the rear of the cave. "We don't know the species of this bat. What should we write for the other team?" one scientist asks.

"What do you think we should do? If we do not know the species, how can we best communicate what we see to the other team?" I ask.

One explorer records data from a cave into their field notebook.

"I'm going to draw and color it," one scientist announces.

"I am going to just describe all the details in sentences. Is that OK?" another scientist asks.

"Of course. Do what you think is best and most helpful for the other team," I answer. As I turn to crawl out, a scientist yells, "Watch out! There are larvae of something right there. You are about to crush them, and they could be poisonous!"

"Well, I am not going to eat them, so poisonous doesn't really matter, right?" I respond.

"Oh, I mean venomous! Also, you don't want to harm them anyway; they could be a new species, Mrs. Schnekser!" the scientist adds.

"You are right. Thanks for the heads-up, teammate!" I reply and exit carefully.

I love crawling into the caves with them, helping spot creatures and listening to their squeals of excitement and surprise when they happen upon large tarantulas and bats hanging from the ceilings of caves or centipedes and cockroaches scaling the walls. We even take cave selfies and videos to document our expedition because, well, why not?

Before we know it, the class is nearly over, and I call all scientists to exit the cave system. I go first and quickly begin recording their exit with my phone. Each scientist exits in their own special style—barrel rolls, forward rolls, dramatic arm reaches and gasping . . .

As we wait for their general education teacher to arrive, we debrief on the caving expedition together in the hallway before sending our data to the other team of scientists. We find areas of discrepancy among our data and varying recollections of the caves and what belongs to each. This is the perfect way to talk about the importance of the organization of data in the field. We will revisit all of this during their next session in the laboratory with me. They will actually analyze the data and draw their own conclusions, extending the expedition into the reporting and sharing phase of science. So much comes out of this simple experience, this simulated field expedition. The process they use, the experience itself, and the data are all authentic the only part that is artificial are the caves themselves. This experience also blends into nonfiction texts about bats, nonfiction text features, history of cave exploration, the geography and geology of cave locations, formation of freshwater aquifers, and statistics. The opportunities this experience creates during and after are plentiful, and we will not even scratch the surface of all of the things I could have integrated.

CREATING MEMORABLE SCIENCE EXPERIENCES

So, how did this all happen? How do I make these experiences happen for my students? Let's rewind about three days . . .

I had this crazy idea in the middle of class one day. My scientists were studying landforms of North America and participating in a postcard exchange with classes around the continent. They had already assembled a wall-sized physical map of North America and were getting a little antsy as they worked on a slideshow about the schools with whom we exchanged postcards and the landforms they were learning about as a result. What do you do?

Well, if you are me, you pull up some photos from college of you spelunking and engage them in a story of the time you were stuck in between a stalactite and a stalagmite. Classic teacher move, right? Tell a story and ambush them with content terminology. You don't do that? You should totally try it; it works every time. With my students on the edge of their seats, partly because of the picture of me dangling upside down in a cave and partly because they wanted to know what happened next, it hit me. I needed to take my scientists spelunking! In that exact moment, I stopped telling my students the story. I became stoic and serious and explained that, on Friday, they would need lights—headlamps, camping lanterns, flashlights, any light they could bring. In my head, I had already planned the system of caves I would be creating in the room. In each cave, there would be hidden creatures for them to count and record. They would navigate through the cave system and complete a biodiversity survey. Sure, this would be a fabricated system of caves, but they would be doing real science, using field protocols and exploring a unique landform in North America. As luck would have it, as soon as I finished my story of surviving Trout Cave in West Virginia, their general classroom teacher returned to take them back to their general education classroom. I reminded them in a serious tone that they needed lights on Friday.

Then, I immediately jumped on Amazon to order bats, centipedes, roaches, beetles, tarantulas, and any other toy replica of cave creatures I could. I contacted my friend and bat conservationist Dr. Kristen Lear to see if she had data about bats within caves I could use to make the experience authentic. I hurried to the supply closet down the hall, stole an excessive amount of brown paper, and chanted, *Nothing to see here,* in my head as I scurried to my classroom to hide my contraband. My plan was to use each lab table in my room as a cave. I would cover three of the four sides with paper for the walls of the caves and stack all of the chairs at the edge of the classroom. Two tables placed together in an L-shape would create a large cave in the back of the room. Each cave would be stocked with its own collection of creatures for our scientists to track and record.

When Friday rolled around, I wore my headlamp all day. My school, colleagues, and students alike should all be used to my antics by now, but they were still taken aback by seeing my hair styled into an unusually high ponytail with a headlamp on my forehead. So many questions! Can't a science teacher just walk around with field equipment on and not be questioned? Nope. I basically denied that anything was unusual, though at lunch, I made sure to visit the third-grade tables and ask them in a bit of an exaggerated tone whether they had remembered their lamps. It's not difficult to excite students in the cafeteria on a Friday, which is also ice cream day, but I did my best to up the ante. I am not sure my colleagues appreciated it, but it sure did set the scene for the afternoon in science.

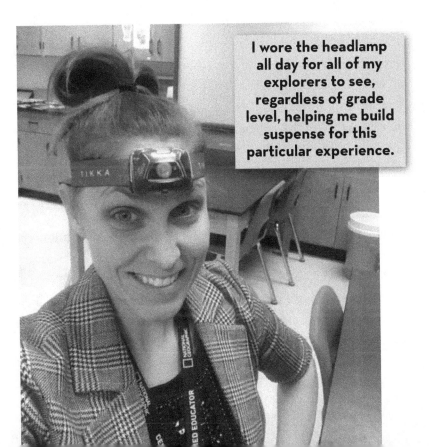

I wore the headlamp all day for all of my explorers to see, regardless of grade level, helping me build suspense for this particular experience.

Science, and I would actually argue all subjects, is not meant to be just received; it is meant to be experienced. That's how we learn as humans. Experiences teach us what to do and what *not* to do. So stop micromanaging, stop lecturing, stop showing videos, stop reading paragraphs, and just do it.

My first graders have to learn about the classification of animals as part of their content strands. They need to know that animals are categorized into different groups, with the two main groups being vertebrates and invertebrates. Generally, vertebrates are easy-peasy—anything with a backbone. Students are masters at naming these, with the exception of miscategorizing snakes as having no backbone. Trust me when I tell you they do not need to practice regurgitating this material. What they do need help understanding and investigating are invertebrates. Even though there are more invertebrates than vertebrates in the world, they can seem less exciting. After all, who doesn't love a cute puppy, cat, monkey, or elephant? Invertebrates are fascinating, though, and easier to find on your campus (even in your building) than vertebrates. Think about it—how many times have you seen a spider or cockroach in your school building or facility? Perhaps you even found them because someone was screaming and running hysterically in the hallway. Don't worry, I won't tell your facilities staff you told me about the spiders, cockroaches, and ants, but we all have seen them, and it's OK. In fact, it's the perfect way to introduce and examine invertebrates.

If you (gasp) go outside with your scientists, you'll find a bounty of insects and other invertebrates just hopping, squirming, digging, and flying all around. How cool would it be to collect them and discover what makes them invertebrates and, even further, insects versus arachnids? Totally cool, so let's do it!

In the transition from summer to fall, my laboratory looks like a botanical garden's butterfly exhibit with enclosures all over the room housing caterpillars, butterflies, moths, spiders, and praying mantises we have found and collected just steps from the school building and sometimes even inside of the building. Can you imagine what we would find, collect, and observe if we took another five steps outside? What about ten? Or even across the soccer field to the collection of walnut trees?

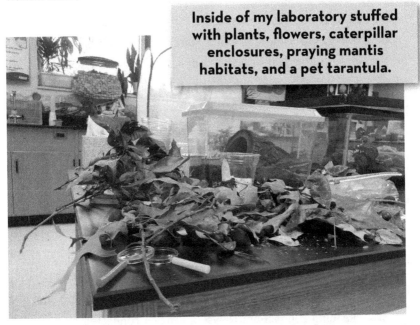

Inside of my laboratory stuffed with plants, flowers, caterpillar enclosures, praying mantis habitats, and a pet tarantula.

That's an experience. Then, what if we took this experience and created a field guide for our campus based on what we found and how many? What if we updated this field guide each year to collect longitudinal data over time? What if we shared what we are doing on social media with local scientists? What if maybe we even published our field guide and made it a part of our library's circulation or reference materials?

Now we're talking about an experience that's cross-curricular. It immerses students within the world of what makes things work and what makes things happen, and they naturally experience all of the details involved within a concept. They will remember that experience, the skills involved, the feelings they felt, and the challenges they overcame. What they learned will be engrained in their whole being, not just in their brain to dump on a test and forget for the next set of content to memorize.

hen I think about experiences, I start with what my students need to get from a unit of study. Whether it's a list of skills, standards, objectives, or a combination of those, I start there and think about what these skills and objectives look like in the world outside of a traditional classroom. Maybe the connection is to social media outlets they are using outside of class, sports, or extra-curricular activities. I often seek ways to connect to careers in science, as well as making the experience span many different facets of life.

My outline of the experience begins to take shape into categories:

- **Experience:** caving
- **Science connection:** landforms, geology, bat ecology and behavior, fieldwork, scientific communication
- **Math connection:** collecting data, graphing data, analyzing data, communicating data to others
- **Writing connection:** descriptive piece detailing this specific experience, communicating an experience in general, technical writing, recalling the event, and communicating data
- **Reading connection:** Newsela articles connected to caves, bats, and bat ecologists, nonfiction text features
- **Art:** cave painting, storytelling through art, comics or graphic novels, illustration for books
- **Social studies and history:** ancient cave paintings, storytelling, archaeology, geography of cave painting, cultural implications of cave painting

By listing all the connections that come to mind when I have an experience or topic in mind, I can then plan accordingly, deciding what topics and skills I will cover, in what order, and what colleagues I can connect with to make deeper connections between our classes or content. I often find then, with these collaborations and conversations, even more connections are created in real time.

Somehow, each day, you remember how to walk, ride a bike, and sign in and out of work, though there was never a test on it. Isn't that interesting? You experienced them, and they became a part of your life and skill set—no traditional multiple-choice, true/false, or essay testing required.

As teachers we must ask: How can we create an experience for our students to navigate that incorporates content standards and skills? Even better, how can we craft an experience that is authentic, something they might actually do in life after traditional schooling that incorporates content knowledge and skills? If possible, the experience should be real, but when that isn't possible, a simulation, like the spelunking I created for my students, works as well, especially when you strive for as much authenticity as possible, like the use of real data in the cave system.

In what ways can and will you create an experience for your students?

Creating experiences might not feel natural or come naturally at first, so what do you do? I asked my friend Anne Lewis to weigh in, and here are her thoughts:

If we want to teach the whole student, this means we have to become the whole teacher, integrating our personal and professional sides. This does not mean you have to become your students' new best friend, but rather that you bring yourself, particularly your passions and interests, to your students. Students often ask, "Why do I have to learn this?" and we as educators usually default to reasons that sound more like platitudes. What would change if we responded, "Because I care deeply about this, and I want you to see how fascinating this is and how the world becomes richer, bigger, and more exciting when you know/can do this." Maybe you don't use those words exactly, but you can convey that attitude.

Good professional development will provide experiences that yield teaching artifacts of pictures, videos, anecdotes, or memorabilia. When this becomes your mindset, what professional development looks like begins to open up. Professional development is no longer just a class, course, or workshop; it's life. It's a family trip to a national park, a paddle on a Saturday afternoon with a friend, a lecture by a favorite author, a visit to a historic site in the next community, or making applesauce from scratch. Any experience you have can also be used to teach students.

It is incumbent on teachers to own their professional learning and seek out those opportunities that will build them into their best teaching selves. Seeking out professional development that provides personally/professionally enriching opportunities that yield teaching stories may not feel significant, but remember: a path that diverges from the main road by a few degrees at the beginning will end up in a different place at the end.

EDUCATOR ASIDE

Elijah Carbajal (@carbaeli)
grade three teacher

Experience-based learning always trumps the traditional lesson approach. Lectures and worksheets do little to nothing to impact student learning, especially in the area of science. My motto when it comes to teaching science is that students need to *experience* science instead of just *reading* about science. My friend and teacher mentor, Tracey Taylor, once told me to give students an experience they can't get from Google. While reading and Google searches have their places in the classroom, they should never be the only approach to teaching.

I first experienced just how powerful giving students an experience can be when I transformed my room into a café. Café Carbajal is what

I called it. The tables were decorated, hot chocolate and snacks served, and smooth jazz was playing in the background. On the ˙ hung my students' abstract art. I, along with two parents who heₗped that day, was dressed in black pants, a white shirt, and a black tie. The purpose was to create a comfortable and fun atmosphere for students to discuss their book study work. The looks on their faces, the sounds of their surprise, and the way they worked that day are things I will never forget. It was an experience that directly impacted student learning. It was an experience they—and I—will never forget!

I knew this was the approach I needed to take when it came to teaching all subjects, but especially science. I did some research and asked for help on Twitter. Becky was the first person to message me with ideas and strategies. At the time, I was teaching about energy. I decided I needed to take this lesson outside. After a short explanation of the difference between potential and kinetic energy, the students were given tablets. Their objective was to film themselves demonstrating the difference between potential and kinetic energy. No other instructions. I left it all up to them. (Teachers, you need to be willing to let go and let the students take over. You'll be surprised and impressed at what they come up with!)

I was amazed by their ideas. Students were hitting tetherballs, jumping off swings, running downhill, and going down the slides. As they performed their demonstrations, they gave commentary on what they were doing and how it related to the potential and kinetic energy. They did all of this with another student recording them. Nothing out of a book. No lecture. Just a brief, maybe five-minute discussion *with my students* about the two types of energy, then all exploration. They shared their videos in our Google Classroom, and as I watched them, I was blown away at just how much knowledge they took away. There was no confusion or misconceptions on their end.

When you give kids a chance to experience science in a hands-on and practical way, their learning is directly impacted for the better. There is no better way to teach science. Yes, you will have to give some explanation, but allow your students to take part in that with you. Last year,

I read *Teach Like a Pirate* by Dave Burgess. It changed the way I look at teaching. In that book, Dave teaches us that part of teaching like a pirate is *immersion*. You have to immerse everyone—yourself and your students—in the learning process. You don't do that by lecturing for an hour or having the kids read out of the book. Your students have to be immersed in the science experience.

This isn't easy. It will take a lot of hard work and mindful reflection on your part as the teacher. Sometimes it takes me hours to develop the experiences I want to give them. However, it does get easier the more you do it. It's a challenge, but the payoff is always worth it. You won't regret giving your students these experiences, and your students will be grateful to you.

As I stated earlier, you have to be willing to let go of control and give it to the students. The tighter the grip you keep on your students, the less impactful the experience will be. Don't worry if your classroom gets a little noisy during these times. Don't worry about how messy things may get. I've had glass jars break while students created mixtures and solutions. (Don't worry; no one was injured. We had safety procedures in place for events like this. Have fun, but remember to be safe.) The science lab got noisy when my students were tapping on jars filled with different liquids, testing the pitch of each one. All of that is OK! Science can be messy at times, but that's just part of the experience.

Experiences are fun. Science is meant to be interactive and engaging. Don't bore your students into hating your science period. How many of your students leave school bummed out because your math lesson went long and you didn't have time for science? How many of those students are disappointed because your lesson was, again, lecture-based? You have students right now who love science and are eager to learn. Give them something fun. Make science exciting! Make your experiences ones they will never forget!

CHAPTER FOUR

THE POWER OF DISCOVERY

"**M**rs. Schnekser, come see this!"

"Look what we found!"

"Did you know this would happen?"

"Look what we can do!"

I walk toward a group of my first-grade scientists as they investigate magnets. They take turns showing me what they have discovered about the little black pieces of hard material I have given them. The properties of the material vary: they are circular, rectangular, broken, chunky, sharp, or smooth. Some have holes in the middle, and some are solid. Each table has an assortment to explore. The students are up, jumping, talking, laughing, sharing, and collaborating, and I have little to nothing to do with it.

"Look, they are playing tag!" one student shouts, as he uses one magnet to "chase" another around the table. Later, I will sneak in the word *repel* to describe this action. I will even throw in "poles" to help my scientists describe the magnets with technical terms. Right now, though, it's about the discovery, exploration, and excitement of something new.

"Mrs. Schnekser, he *stole* my magnet!" another student exclaims across the room. Although I now need to help two scientists resolve conflict, they have just discovered the "attraction" of two magnets. Perfect. As I walk over, I think about how I am going to reframe this for the visibly upset scientist whose magnet was "stolen."

"Oh my gosh, you know what we can do now? Let's figure out how to steal the magnet back using one of these extra pieces!" I say in a mischievous voice. She grins and grabs a new magnet and uses it to attract the two magnets from her classmate. I stay close because this is for sure going to cause a ruckus.

"Hey! That's *mine!*" he yells, and I quickly jump in.

"Oh snap! Did you see what happened? You originally used your magnet to *attract* hers, then she grabbed a new magnet and used it to *attract* it back! This is what I like to call an 'epic science battle,' muha-hahahahaha," I say in a dramatic movie voice.

The crisis is averted, and I even sneak in a science term. I also take the magnets apart and give them back to each scientist, and in departing from their table, I say, "I wonder if you could make a game out of that discovery . . ." I do not turn around to see their reaction, but I hear bodies scurrying around the table behind me and can only assume they took the challenge bait!

THE CHOOSE-YOUR-OWN-JOURNEY METHOD OF TEACHING SCIENCE

It's during times like these that I realize the power of discovery, redirection, and reframing in the world of education. The first step, though, is opening up yourself, your classroom, and your curriculum to allow for discovery and exploration time. Time will always be a challenge, but we cannot continue to use it as an excuse for lame teaching methods and strategies. Rather, we must find a way to redirect, reframe, and discover for ourselves how to make this happen for our learners. It is 100 percent worth it.

When students have time to explore and discover concepts you were going to teach them anyway, they have a better connection with the material. *They* played, *they* observed, *they* learned, and *they* made the connections. You were only there to interject the technicalities and terms and plant additional seeds that allow that initial discovery to go in the direction your content standards require. You are a master gardener; you plant the seeds and see what germinates. If your crop is not yielding the necessary fruit, you add nutrients and supplements, you plow and use different and new tools to ensure success. You don't want your proverbial garden to be unsuccessful, so you do what it takes to get the results you desire and meet your curriculum demands. This is your role as the educator in the room. Use the best tools and tap into natural curiosity and our desire to explore and discover. If that doesn't take learning far enough, then you come in and supplement. That initial exploration and discovery is hugely important, though. Not only are you allowing students time to connect with the material and make discoveries, but you are also empowering them to explore, ask questions, and attempt to find the answers on their own. This is science in its purest form.

I often initially teach my students with the barest essential materials and concrete plans. This does not mean I have no plan; that I have no explicit outcomes, goals, or objectives; or that I do not know where I intend to lead my scientists. In fact, to do this, I actually have over-planned, over-gathered materials, and overthought everything. That's OK because for true discovery or inquiry-based teaching to occur, all those things are essential. The beauty and often scary part of this method is trusting it will end up the way it needs to and not knowing the exact path you and your learners will take to reach your intended outcomes. I think of it, honestly, like a "choose your own journey" novel. These were all the rage when I was little. I remember in fourth grade, our read-alouds were these types of books; we even read the same book several times, choosing different adventures each time just to see the different outcomes. In not knowing exactly which direction your learners will go through their discovery, you must be prepared to follow, which means you have indeed overplanned and overthought in anticipation of where your young scientists will go and what they will need along the journey.

Let me share an example of how I approach a new unit. My second graders study electricity and circuits, so I begin with each student grabbing a battery and either an alarm bell or motor. The alarm and motor have two attached wires that are color-coded red and black. I simply tell students to "make them work." What I know is that the alarm bell has polarity, while the motor does not. Mostly, the first investigation is about watching what they do, what they know, and how they react, especially when facing adversity. I usually sit in the middle of the room and let students work. I listen, watch, and say very little. If they find themselves not enjoying the experiment or finding initial success, my response is "Try something new" or "Show me what you have tried so far."

A team of second-grade scientists explores with two wires, one light bulb, and a battery.

Usually, by this time, a few students have figured it out or got lucky in making the motor spin or alarm sound. My next move is to have them draw what worked in their journals then try the item they have not yet used. After they find success with both items, I ask them to bring me their journals and materials, and I try to recreate their drawings with the materials. This is a great opportunity to teach them about effective communication. They often laugh when I can't make the circuit work, and we share a laugh about their drawing. They immediately grab their notebooks and change their drawings to be more accurate without any direction from me at all. Magic.

What happens in these moments determines what materials come out next. You see, I *did* overplan, I *did* overthink, and I *did* pull out an overabundance of materials—all because I did not (and never do!) know what direction this was going to take.

Do they all have electrical engineer parents who have taught them this already? Will they need more experience in tinkering? Do they know how to coach one another? How do they persevere in the face of adversity? What words are they using?

There is so much to consider here, and every year is different. Heck, every class is different. Class one of second grade might need completely different things than the class that comes in next. The beauty of discovery or inquiry-based teaching is that you can assess so many things at the same time. Another beauty, although intimidating and messy, is the opportunity to differentiate and address all learners where they need to be met. This gets chaotic, and there is no way around it, but it is what's best for my learners, so I commit wholeheartedly to these methods.

Figuring Out What to Use to Teach during a Unit, on the Fly

I begin every unit with an exploration of materials. For electricity, that is two wires, one light bulb, and one battery. As my scientists explore these materials with the simple direction of "Make the light bulb illuminate," I am observing how they explore the materials, what words they use, what ideas they try, what makes them frustrated, etc.

At the same time, I am thinking about all of the experiences (activities or lessons) we could possibly do to learn about electricity. If there are concepts, skills, or ideas they already "get" in the initial exploration, I can mark them off on my matrix. I know I do not need to do every single experience for that skill set. If they need more experience, I use the activities specifically for the skills and knowledge they are lacking. Below is an abbreviated sample matrix to show you how I use this type of chart for instructional decision-making. Some years, I have to use all experiences; other years, it is far less. It depends on what I observe for my learners. Sometimes only a small part of the class does a certain activity because it is what they need.

Having a matrix like this for every unit was very helpful, but it can be time consuming. It's a goal, not a requirement, so if this feels overwhelming, try it with one unit and build from there if you find it helpful. You might use something different altogether to make decisions or perhaps even nothing at all. But I challenge you to really look at all of the possible experiences you can provide your students within a unit and determine, based on formative assessments, what your learners actually need. They may need every lesson, but you might just find that they don't. This will help you hone your own craft and save that precious time we often find we never have enough of.

	Light Lab 1	Light Lab 2	Switch Lab	Paper Circuit	Baggie Investigation	Safety Simulation
Build a series circuit	X			X		
Build a parallel circuit		X		X		
Connect that the battery is the power source	X	X	X	X		
Connect that wires carry electrical currents	X	X	X	X		
Identify conductors					X	
Identify insulators						X
Identify open vs. closed circuits	X	X	X	X	X	X

All of my scientists will be creating circuits, electrical diagrams, and eventually a larger-scale project, which requires them to use this knowledge to solve a real-world problem. Over the years, we have done this in so many ways. Sometimes scientists create model houses (dollhouses, but I don't like to call them that) with functioning light switches and circuits. Sometimes they create greeting cards with lighting features when you open them. Other times, they create a quiz or review game where they construct circuits that light up when the correct answer is chosen. This all depends on the scientist. Sometimes they have a choice of what to create; again, this is all dependent on what they do during the unit. Most often, each class has a different task to complete because that's how the chips fall. That's where their skills and interests aligned—same content standards, different journeys.

Not only does this type of pedagogy lend itself to meeting learners where they are, but it is also highly engaging and allows for a great deal of student voice and choice. Their buy-in is very important. People of all ages produce better products when they feel connected and a part of the process. Why *not* do this with your learners?

A second-grade scientist begins adding circuits to a model home they designed and built.

Throwing students into situations with very little direction might seem risky, but I can tell you from my experience with students in grades pre-K through grade five and in all subjects, the risk and scariness of the "disorder" in the room is worth every second. This type of work offers natural formative assessment at every given moment, promotes student buy-in and engagement, and ultimately connects students closely to how the skills they are learning are relevant in their lives.

EDUCATOR ASIDE

Paula Huddy-Zubkowski (@littlephz)

K–12 instructional media and ed tech consultant and Educator Explorer

The power of discovery has propelled the human story through the ages. In the process of discovering, we have learned about the environment and ourselves through curiosity and observation. I think children have a natural advantage, being delightfully curious in the small and inconspicuous, and at the same time, I am often taken aback by the powerful big ideas and connections they can make. Early in my teaching career, I might have started a lesson by standing at the front of my second graders and enthusiastically declaring, "Today we are going to investigate blubber!" But after more than fourteen years of teaching, I have harnessed the power of discovery.

One year during our trout rearing project, instead of telling my students the reason why there was polystyrene attached to the aquarium, I set them up to discover for themselves what the purpose was. Later in the week, I invited students to submerge one hand into a bag of ice-cold water and the other hand into a bag of butter. I wanted them to hypothesize what was happening and use their senses to compare how each hand felt. Could this resemble something in nature? How does this work? I also wanted to provoke their curiosity. Students began to investigate. They touched, tested, and kept revisiting the butter. They looked at the aquarium and said, "Maybe it is something like polystyrene?" I facilitated classroom conversations with expert divers who spoke about the water ecosystem and scuba diving gear.

When a diver asked the students why they might need to wear a wet suit suddenly someone yelled, "Yes, it's insulation so you don't get cold. Maybe it is like blubber?!" Other students bantered back and forth until, as a class, we thought that was a logical answer. My students excitedly connected their background knowledge and investigative skills and made the connection that the butter mimicked blubber in an insulating capacity like the divers' wet suits and the polystyrene on the tank; it was a real *Magic School Bus* moment!

As my students began to understand insulation, they were then able to relate to Arctic animals, water cycles, buoyancy, and so many more ideas. Students then questioned how the divers used a remotely operated vehicle (ROV) to study shipwrecks. They wondered if we could design and build our own. I had no idea how this would work, but together as a community of learners, we investigated this new discovery. By connecting students to explorers, experts, ROV webcams of animals, and so much more, students engaged in design thinking principles, which helped them make real-world connections to learning standards and curriculum. Giving students materials and items, they began to test and build diverse ROV prototypes. They used the information from the expert we had met, and many began to research and try to find what could help keep the ROV balanced. With time to reflect and engage in sustained project development, the students were able to design and test their own floating ROV with a GoPro camera catching all the action.

What some may see as chaos in the classroom is a magical journey of learning for my students. With curiosity as our catalyst, there is one more secret ingredient needed for powerful discovery: time. The process of discovery leads to the possibility of countless spirals of inquiry, generating endless streams of wonder and exploration. Whether students explore the outdoors or use materials within the classroom, we need to give them time and more time to think for themselves. Give students voice and choice in their learning, which requires more time. When educators center the learners' lenses of observation in the classroom and beyond, intrinsic motivation to seek and discover are ignited within each student.

I am no longer hesitant to invest time into the process of curiosity-fueled discovery; I have been blown away by the return on investment. This is truly the secret to learning that transforms. Young people are such wonderfully curious souls who continue to want to explore and discover. I love the quote by Chris Lehman from the book *Launch into Design Thinking* by John Spencer that says, "If you assign a project and get back thirty of the exact same thing, that's not a project. That's a recipe." I see curiosity, discovery, and time as a triple Venn diagram, with the learner in the middle. So much possibility to cultivate questions and connections is generated by these overlapping spaces, and this is where the learning journey is centered in my work with students.

CHAPTER FIVE

VOICE AND CHOICE

"**W**hat do you mean, interactive?" asks one of my scientists. "Do you mean like the way you teach us stuff?" a second scientist asks.

"Can I just make a poster?" inquires another.

"Interactive means we all participate as we learn. And no, posters are boring. Give us something to remember!" I respond. "Show me what you can come up with here that teaches us about your inventor and requires that we all participate!"

And with that, they're off. Some are excited, motivated, and inspired, while others are confused, scared, and a little worried about what this will all mean and look like in the end. No matter their state of mind, they all set to work. Their task is to learn about a Black inventor and create an experience to teach the rest of us about them.

Two weeks later, long strings of gold and black tinsel hang from our classroom door frame and glisten, basically begging for us to walk through. Skylar, a fourth grader, greets us at the door, welcoming us to the party.

"This party is in honor of Madam C.J. Walker. Please come in!" Skylar says.

Skylar welcomes fellow students into her celebration of Madam C. J. Walker

While we wait our turn to enter, we all try to peek beyond the elegant door decoration to see what's inside the party room. As each student disappears beyond the gold and black tinsel curtain, audible gasps of excitement fill the air.

I am the last to enter, and I find my students scoping out the different stations set up around the room. Skylar gathers us all together to explain the stations. At station one, we find a table covered in large white feathers, bowties, and fake pearl necklaces. Skylar explains to us how Madam Walker began her own business in the early 1900s, providing better beauty and hair products for African American women. All of the photographs she found of Madam Walker showed her in a pearl necklace, usually with a feather in her hair. She also noticed that most men wore bowties in the photographs, but Skylar says that anyone can use any of the items at the table to get into the theme of the party!

At station two, we can have our hair styled by Skylar, and nearly everyone, including me, takes advantage! Many of those large white feathers from station one end up in our hairdos! While we enjoy this station, Skylar explains to us that Madam Walker made her business based on beauty products for Black women, focusing on hair and how to style it, which was the inspiration for creating this station.

At station three, another student, Sophia, has collaborated with Skylar to set up an entertainment station where we can play the game hot potato to honor her inventor, George Crum, the inventor of the potato chip. I love this collaboration, which came about organically from these two students having a genuine conversation and choosing to work together—no forced teams here.

During the event, students also grab iPads to take pictures and videos. They want to capture the action and make a movie about it afterward. *Whaaat?* I think to myself. This is in no way prompted by me; I am a literal spectator as this all unfolds. I participate and enjoy the event as it happens. I am not teaching directly, I am not in charge, and I am not telling anyone what to do. This is all the authentic engagement of my scientists. All I did was empower them to create interactive experiences as a way to teach others about the amazing accomplishments of Black inventors. My scientists literally did everything from research to planning and implementing experiences to documenting it. Not only did they choose these aspects of their own projects, but they were also free to choose how to participate. This purposeful decision on my part put these students at ease and, dare I say, allowed them to enjoy learning about their inventors and those their classmates studied. They did not have to sit in neatly arranged rows as they heard classmate after classmate regurgitate facts and display a poster about their historic figure.

The simple decision to allow student voice and choice made a huge difference in the delivery of this project from start to finish. It probably doesn't hurt that they see me take this interactive and immersive approach in my own teaching. I am not saying that to toot my own horn here; it's literally what one of my young scientists asked as I finished giving directions: "Do you mean like the way you teach us stuff?"

My friend Tracey Taylor, who's an elementary art teacher in New Mexico, offers the following reflection and questions to guide your own thinking to employ student voice and choice:

Partnering with students can be a powerful tool for teachers. Mindfully considering student voice and choice can bring students to the table as active shareholders in their achievement and success. Are you reteaching what they already know or understand? Could our twenty-first-century students get the same thing you are serving up in your classrooms with a simple Google search or by asking Alexa for an answer? Have you created a space and place in which they feel comfortable with inquiry or complex application?

HANDING OVER THE KEYS TO YOUR STUDENTS

Student voice and choice releases creativity, freedom of expression, and a challenge to be better. It's helpful when you are the first to be creative so when you release your learners to be creative and use their voice and choice, they have a great model to follow. They know they can and should take risks; it's the expectation.

When you take risks, your learners will, too. When you think differently, your learners will, too. When you express your voice, your learners will, too. Expect more out of yourself to expect more from your students. We don't need any more encyclopedias; we need thinkers, changemakers, and explorers.

You know where your learners need to be in terms of content—the final destination, so to speak. How they get to that point can and should be an opportunity for creativity, detours, rest stops, collaboration, consultation, mistakes, and deep learning. They need to make decisions in terms of their own learning and demonstration of knowledge. This learning can and should happen in a way that best suits each student. Sometimes this will overlap between different learners, while other times it will feel like a fifty-ring circus, but the important part is not how *you* feel; it's how your *learners* feel, how *they* are progressing, and how *they* are connecting with the content. They need to feel free—no, empowered—to use their voice and choice in your learning environment.

———

"Mrs. Schnekser, can I update the trout Instagram?" one scientist asks.

"What about when we take the expedition? Can I update our social media while we are out there?" another eager scientist follows.

"I'd rather blog today. Can I post updates there instead of recording a podcast episode?" a third scientist adds.

"The three of us are going to team up today and record a podcast about trout development. Where can we go to record?" an eager threesome shouts.

For the entirety of our watershed rehabilitation project, my scientists have been maintaining logs of water quality, trout development, and new content learned through blog posts, podcast episodes, tweets, and a dedicated Instagram account. They love having the freedom and ability to choose which platform they use each day. Sometimes every platform is updated on the same day by different scientists, and sometimes they join together to use just one platform. Part of the beauty of this is that students choose how to use their voice and often debate which platform is the best for a particular status update. This is a great critical thinking exercise since different social media platforms have different advantages. Instagram is known for visuals as the main attraction, whereas Twitter is better known for short word or phrase-based sharing. Blogs are all about longer text-based sharing, and podcasts are about audio and the art of oral storytelling and conversation. Based on the learning that happens each day and the highlights these scientists choose to share, students must weigh their options.

"I don't really have a lot to share today. I think we should take a great picture and post it with a short caption," one scientist remarks.

"Yeah, we can post it on Twitter and Instagram and not have to worry about trying to make a whole podcast episode with not a lot to really share," another scientist agrees. Then off they walk to the iPads to post their observation of the day.

The trout Instagram account is one of my favorites because my scientists do not update as humans; they take on the role of the trout when they post their pictures, captions, and creative hashtags. In 2018, their blog about this project earned them an underwater ROV (remotely operated vehicle) from Sofar (sofarocean.com). That underwater ROV has been driven by my scientists in pools, local estuaries, the Chesapeake Bay, and even the Florida Keys! Just by using their own voice to share with the world, this opportunity presented itself. Of course, getting free gear and gadgets is not what it's all about, although it is an amazing perk that all of my scientists have enjoyed as a result. Rather, using social media platforms and different ways of communicating has fostered better communication among my scientists and empowered them to share their stories, experiences, scientific knowledge, data, and conclusions. In sharing all of this information, they are participating in discussions about scientific content, which is a sneaky teacher move, if I dare say so myself. This simple shift in my instruction

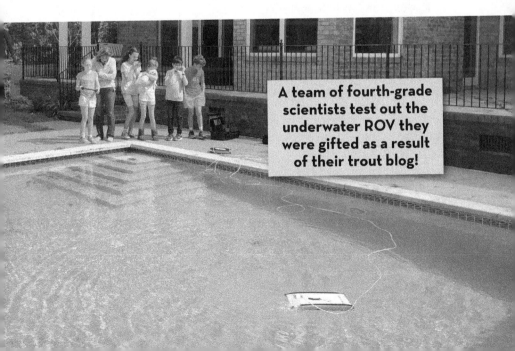

A team of fourth-grade scientists test out the underwater ROV they were gifted as a result of their trout blog!

has made a huge difference in how my scientists internalize content rather than just receive, memorize, then dump it after an assessment.

I made the conscious decision to move into sharing scientific content through these common social media platforms for a few different reasons I believe make a powerful shift in thinking for educators and scientists alike, opening both of these groups to the reality that communication, and even scientific communication, can be done effectively through social media platforms. If we use the same communication methods as the general public and our learners, chances are communication will be more widely spread and perhaps even read! For my learners, this shift in communicating within science class via a social media platform was a hook to relevance. Students are using these platforms each day outside of class. They read blogs, listen to podcasts, watch endless YouTube videos, and post to and follow Instagram, Twitter, and TikTok feeds. They know how these platforms work and how to navigate them, and more important, they *want* to use them. It is true that perhaps not every single student is using them, especially at the elementary level, but I bet you they have heard of them. If they have never heard of these social media platforms, then you have the opportunity to introduce them to new avenues of communication. How exciting! Whether students have already engaged in these social media platforms or are introduced to them through your class, these platforms provide great entry points to promote sharing scientific content and practicing important communication skills in a way that is relevant to our students. This brings me to my second reason for integrating these platforms with my learners: communication skills. These are the avenues in which adults and youth alike are communicating their thoughts and learning. In utilizing these platforms for students to share content, we are teaching them different communication skills, as well as the safe navigation of the internet and social media. This is embedded or sometimes referred to as hidden curriculum—bonus opportunities to educate about relevant topics that are not specifically tied to our content standards but are natural integrations that occur.

Why *wouldn't* we take advantage? Because it's difficult to prepare, difficult to manage, or not a content standard you need to cover? Stop right now with the excuses.

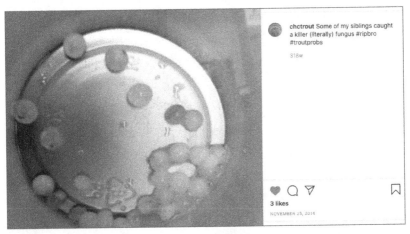

chctrout Some of my siblings caught a killer (literally) fungus #ripbro #troutprobs

318w

3 likes

NOVEMBER 25, 2014

This is not something new you have to dream up. These tools are replacements for outdated methods. These student-created productions can even be used as your formative and summative assessments for content standards. These are authentic pieces of work your students have created—assess them here and now. Another sneaky teacher move.

Chances are your students are already using these platforms to *consume* content, so why not use it to have them *create* content of their own? As an added bonus, the content they are sharing is what they are doing and learning, the data they are collecting, and the conclusions they are drawing. This is a component of science that is largely overlooked and even purposefully omitted in science classrooms for many reasons. Oftentimes the excuse is time. Let me put into writing a truth bomb that is not always easy to admit or even say out loud: we make time for things that are important.

You have to recognize that this piece, communication, is important. *You* have to make a change. *You* need to stop using time as an excuse. There are so many ways to make time, create cohesive, cross-curricular connections, empower students to take ownership, and alleviate the "time" it takes for this necessary component of science.

Social Media Opportunities to Share Classroom Content

Social media platforms change often, and it is possible what I publish below will be outdated by the time my book is published, so use this as a springboard for your own ideas.

Whether you use your social media to highlight classroom ed-ventures (see what I did there?) or you want to venture into student generated content, here are some ideas:

- **Instagram:** Perfect for using photos to illustrate ideas, provide updates on projects, or maintain an account as a historical figure or even classroom pet. My scientists maintained one as our classroom trout tank, providing daily updates on their tank events and even creating their own hashtags to go along with posts.

- **Zigazoo:** This is an educator-created app that uses the same premise as the popular TikTok app. It's perfect for educational settings where users can create short videos to illustrate an idea, process, or skill. Teachers can create topics for students to respond to or leave it open-ended for students.

- **Twitter:** With the character limit of Twitter, this is a great way to have students summarize an activity, idea, skill, or event from the classroom. They can take over your teacher Twitter account, or you can create one specifically for your classroom. I allow students to "take over" my Twitter handle. It gives their posting a little excitement and connects to "social media takeovers" they see in popular culture.

- **Facebook:** While this may now be a platform for "old people," as students might lament, this is actually a great opportunity to take on the persona of a significant figure within science, create "groups" for scientists to join, or even parody events that poke a little fun or weave in humor to science. For example: skydiving or bungee jumping with Sir Isaac Newton to prove his laws of motion.

- **Blog:** Using the internet as a platform for student writing is one of the most relevant integrations of communication and social media available. Blogging is literally just writing in electronic form, right? Having a blog could even serve as a portfolio for growth in writing and changes of attitudes, perceptions, and opinions on different topics directly related to classroom content or not. Within the science classroom, what better way could your scientists share an experiment, invention, prototype, problem/solution simulation, or their thoughts on different scientific theories or contrasting work of different scientists? My fourth-grade scientists studying the water quality of the Chesapeake Bay watershed were given an underwater ROV as result of them sharing their study, observations to date, and hopes for future observations. Having scientific communication spread via social media opens up great opportunities, maybe even a donated piece of scientific equipment from a fan!

- **YouTube:** This is probably the way most of our learners, and humans in general, spend time. Whether watching tutorials, parody videos, or vlogs (video blogs), this is a great way to tap into relevance with your learners. My own two children, seven and nine, pretend most of the day to be on a live YouTube stream, complete with "Click to subscribe" and "Comment below if . . ." commentary. Having a class YouTube channel for your learners to create and share content is an easy relevance and tech integration opportunity.

I teach a lot of students—six grade levels to be exact. It would be incredibly easy for me to assign tasks that are the same for every student to complete, assess on a standardized rubric, and call it a day, but notice that's what would be easy for *me*, not what is best for learners or each individual in my laboratory. There is a stark difference here. Sure, I guide them, push them, challenge them, and plant seeds for thought and consideration, but the majority of decisions are in their hands: how to learn and experience content and, ultimately, how they show me they learned something and met the standards we have targeted.

One secret is that I do not allow mediocrity, not for myself and not for my students. They know it, although they will challenge it and sometimes even ask if they can "just make a poster." My response is always the same: "Is that really your best effort? Is that really showing me, in the best way possible, what you have learned and experienced?"

Some students will need scaffolding, perhaps a menu of choices to choose from when it comes to learning and showing their knowledge. Having to make choices and use their own voice can be uncomfortable. This is partly because traditional education has not put them in the position to make these types of decisions on their own. They haven't had an arsenal of educators asking them to think critically. Rather, their arsenal of educators has been teaching them to be consumers of content, receivers instead of thinkers, creators, doers. They will need help, but I am telling you that once you open that door for them, it will be like discovering a new island all their own, and they will forever be changed. They will be empowered. They will be unstoppable. Isn't that what we want? We want to wind them up like a good, old-fashioned wind-up car and let them go to chart their own course and seek ways to learn and do something with what they have learned. We want them to be changemakers, disruptors, and forces for positive momentum in a world that we know all too well to be overwhelming and filled with problems begging to be solved with innovation.

You have the power to open your students' minds to choose their adventure and use their voice to express themselves in whatever unique ways they can muster. Let them figure out who they are through your mentorship.

EDUCATOR ASIDE

Jennifer Appel (@jennifermappel)

educator, author, speaker, blogger, co-creator of *Award Winning Culture*,
and chief heart officer on the Teach Better Team

Reaching twenty-first-century learners requires us to reimagine our educational mindset. In *Award Winning Culture*, my husband and collaborator, Hans Appel, discusses the concept of classroom leader versus classroom manager. I completely agree with this idea that, as an educator, you need to lead learners instead of managing students. While classroom management came easy for me, the transition to becoming a classroom leader required me to step outside my comfort zone to seek direct input from my learners. Viewing my students as the leaders in their own learning meant reshaping projects, instruction, and feedback, which resulted in a remarkable innovative transformation toward student agency.

I remember feeling perfectly aligned to the theory and applications found within George Couros's *The Innovator's Mindset* and David Geurin's *Future Driven* as a way to make sense of my desire to think of my own work through the lens of my learners. These books reinforced the connection between student agency and student voice, and after reading them, I quickly reworked my entire classroom. One of my most successful endeavors has been the *Award Winning Culture* student-led podcast that my husband and I have partnered on. Our student-led podcast explores character, excellence, and community with some of the best leadership minds. Students interview authors, educators, and experts from around the country to gain insights about raising education to amazing heights. In *All In: Taking a Gamble in Education* by Kristen Nan and Jacie Maslyk, Hans reinforces the impact the podcast had on our kids when he writes, "When we cash in on life's opportunities and willingly lean in to professional risk-taking, we have the chance to forever shatter the ceiling on student voice." From the very beginning of this life-changing project, I started to see how amplifying student voice and empowering student agency had a direct effect on leadership. In other words, taking the risk to pivot from manager to leader fostered the same transformation within my students. No longer was I asking them to manage their behavior. They were taking it upon themselves to lead meaningful work. And as I'd quickly learned, positive behavior was a wonderful byproduct of this experiential project.

About six months ago, I was presenting to a group of educators about the inner workings of our student-led podcast. One of the educators in our session asked about cell phones and how we deal with that. Do we have to set rules and expectations for cell phone use during these live recording sessions? I remember distinctly looking at my husband with a blank stare (the kind when someone starts talking to you like you are old friends and you have no idea who they are). He looked back at me with the same look, and I thought we were in trouble. We had never even thought about cell phones until the educator asked about it. We both said, "Nothing." We have never actually even thought about it. Our students don't have a shoe rack or some sort of charging station for cell phones; they just simply come in and start recording. They are podcast leaders being led by a classroom leader (me). But it's not as if they are just busy and don't have time for their phones. In fact, they use their phones to research guests, write notes on interview questions, post social media content, and even communicate recording needs within a session. This object of distraction in some classrooms has become an innovative learning tool in this setting.

Furthermore, the leadership and learning outcomes of amplifying student voice to an authentic audience became crystal clear when we had Charles Tillman (former NFL All-Pro cornerback for the Chicago Bears) on the show. One of our football-playing podcasters lobbied for Tillman's participation and was overjoyed when Tillman agreed to be interviewed prior to Super Bowl LIII. The former pro athlete had just written a chapter book about his childhood and football and graciously sent copies to our students. I gave copies to all three boys. No expectations. No assignment. No requirements. Just "Here's the book, and this is the date of the interview." As you might suspect, one of my boys didn't like to read, told me he hated reading, didn't read for school, and so on. Any guess which boy? Yeah, our football podcaster. Over the next few weeks, every single time I saw him, he'd tell me how much he had read from the book, what questions he'd generated, and what his thoughts were. By the time the interview came, he had finished the entire book. And while I asked him follow-up questions and congratulated him on his accomplishment, he received no grade for finishing it. Because we run this group like a genius hour, student learning is not tied to a formal grade.

When we started the interview, it was a video Skype call so they could all see Tillman for some chitchatting prior to diving into intentional questions. First thing out of Tillman's mouth was, "Hey! What did you think about the book?" For the next couple minutes, the student shared their thoughts about Tillman overcoming racism, as well as the trials and tribulations of frequent childhood moves as a military family. The entire conversation was unplanned, unrehearsed, and unsuspected. Doing the unassigned self-chosen homework of reading the book had a *real-world* application to our students because they *wanted* to learn. It required no worksheets, teacher instruction, or assessment. This is what student voice is all about! I love creating joy-filled cultures of learning where students take control over their life.

How can we transfer this type of real-world, relevant learning to other subject areas, like science, history, language arts, and math? Sometimes it's less about creating and more about *inspiring* these moments. A while back, I was teaching about ancient Greece and I was talking about Athens and how women had some rights, but they were definitely not equal to men. One of my students was absolutely appalled by this and started doing some research on her own. She came back the next day and informed the class that women do not get equal pay to men in the USA, and she had just come to realize this and had all of this research and articles she was going to read and study about the subject. Giving her the floor to present, share, and invite classroom discussion meant that her self-paced learning was both supported by me *and* modeled as a template for others to pursue passion projects. Facilitating student leadership through a learner-driven lens inspires other learners to make connections. Thus, student voice leads to meaningful learning.

When educators listen to their students and let them discover and learn things that are relevant to them, excellence becomes the standard. This is what true voice and choice is all about: students taking on a subject that is important to them and learning everything they can about it. We have to let our students drive the content, expression, and reflection of learning. Outstanding educators infuse voice, leadership, and agency into all aspects of learning. And when students learn in a joy-filled atmosphere, we cultivate our own Award Winning Culture.

CHAPTER SIX

IT'S ALIVE! THE POWER OF LIVE SPECIMEN

"They're on the move!" one scientist exclaims as three of them run toward one of the butterfly habitats, getting on their hands and knees to see monarch caterpillars scaling the sides of the netting.

"Look at the plants! They're complete stubs now!" two scientists shout as they rush to the second butterfly habitat to see the milkweed plants, or what is left of them after being feasted upon by the caterpillars overnight.

"Oh my gosh, is it *dead*?" a scientist inquires, kneeling on top of the closest table to the butterfly habitat, gazing at a caterpillar hanging upside down from the top netting.

"Whoa! Watch it eat the grasshopper's guts!" yells a scientist whose nose is pressed against the praying mantis habitat adjacent to the caterpillars. Four scientists immediately rush over, vying for "nose space" along the habitat's walls.

"It's acting weird. What's happening, Mrs. Schnekser?" another scientist asks as one caterpillar begins spinning as if in a trance as it hangs from the ceiling of one of the butterfly habitats.

"Can we feel them?"

"Can we measure them?"

"Can we take pictures and compare them to last class?"

Third-grade scientists observe monarch caterpillars cultivated from campus and protected as they metamorphosize in the laboratory to be tagged and released once they emerge from their chrysalises.

I am losing track of which scientists are asking questions as I listen to the excitement, watch their interactions, and hop from small group to small group answering questions as fast as I possibly can. These first-grade scientists aren't necessarily studying this content. In other words, this is not what I had planned for today, but this has caught their attention, they are actively engaged, and I am going to use it to segue into what we *are* studying.

If you can't beat 'em, join 'em.

BRINGING LIFE INTO THE LABORATORY

Sometimes you have to use what you've got. Sometimes a lesson goes exactly as planned, and other times you have to be a little creative to get where you need to be with your learners. Sometimes it's as simple as saying "yes" to whatever piques your learners' interests and using that engagement to support and lead your learners to and through the content standards or skill set your curriculum requires.

One thing is for certain: living things, especially animals, get the attention of learners of all ages. Whether they are crawling on the walls of your school building, sneaking into your house on a rainy day, or soaring through the sky, living things are captivating. Let's take a look at some examples of how I integrate living things into my laboratory.

Worms

Worms provide a great opportunity to bridge the study of living and nonliving things with my kindergarten scientists. I am able to introduce concepts of classification and taxonomy, which my scientists then experience in first grade. Whether you dig for worms on your campus or purposefully cultivate them in the classroom, worms will pique the interest of even the most hesitant learners and provide instant reactions and engagement, ranging from disgust to delight. Each time we encounter worms, you would think I gave my five-year-old scientists soda laced with candy. Their squeals of excitement and discovery can be heard throughout the science building. I love seeing them really observe, use related vocabulary, and ask questions. And oh, what questions they have, starting with, "Can we touch them?"

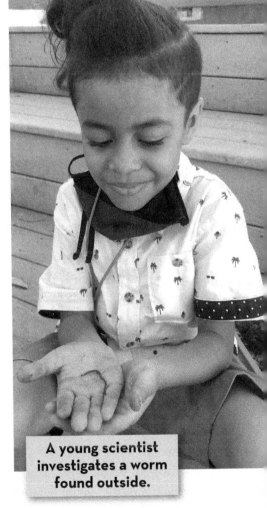

A young scientist investigates a worm found outside.

"Yep," I enthusiastically reply.

And they do. They observe, poke, pick up, bury, and kiss red wiggler and earthworms. We explore the life cycle and classification of worms as living things, as well as the living versus nonliving components of a habitat they must create to sustain life in our laboratory. This all begins through their curiosity and ability to investigate. They start with, "Is it living or nonliving?" but then expand their thinking far beyond that.

These are kindergarten scientists. Can you imagine the places you can take older learners with a simple jumping-off point with worms? Could you talk evolution, adaptation, soil composition, and comparisons between species . . . ?

Beetles

The first year I used beetles to learn with my scientists, you should have seen their eyes light up at the sight of these creatures with pincers and wings and heard their shrieks of joy when they attempted to pick them up and saw the beetle legs squirming to grasp something. My scientists realized instantly whether they were destined for entomology—and there were a few! Those were the scientists who allowed these intriguing creatures to climb all about their hands, arms, and clothing. Those not destined for the field of entomology observed intently but did not engage in observation through touch, which is totally fine and definitely not an expectation. Every scientist learns differently, and this was a perfect example of that.

These beetles had an impact far beyond my kindergarten and first-grade scientists, for whom I purchased them for study. The sight of the new habitat caught the attention of every class. Every. Class.

I think the natural reactions of educators (myself included) is to steer students away from possible distractions. I could have said, "Noneya, none ya bizness," "That is for the transition class," "We are studying something else; that's not for you," or any number of "Pay no attention to the man behind the curtain" tactics, but the truth of the matter is they wanted to know. They were curious. They are scientists. This is a natural part of being human and our thirst for knowledge, and my classroom climate cultivates and encourages this habit of questioning, curiosity, and investigation.

So, what do I do? I do not tweak the curricula of other grade levels, but I do take a break to feed their curiosity and observe their interactions. I use this time to formatively assess their observation skills and devise a way to use these beetles to connect with their content. In fact, I have contemplated permanently altering experiences for students to integrate beetles every year. After all, couldn't my third-grade scientists investigate what types of landforms harbor different beetle species, and couldn't my fourth-grade geologists study what types of rock formations are typically home to beetles? Could we investigate different species of beetles and their respective locations in North America (grade three) and Europe (grade four)? Though my curriculum must cover specified content standards and skills, there are many ways to do that. Tapping into students' natural curiosity is a great place to start.

A young scientist investigates beetles, allowing them to crawl on their shirt.

Fish

For ten years now, I have used fish to enhance learning across grade levels. From life cycles to water chemistry to watershed studies, fish can be the engagement bait. Pun totally intended.

There is a North America-wide initiative called Trout in the Classroom, in which students are tasked with raising a region-specific trout species in their classroom and releasing it into the wild as a culminating event meant to help bolster these native fish populations. For me, this is the perfect way to explore geography, species variation, freshwater versus saltwater fish species, adaptations, watersheds, global climate change indicators, water chemistry, macroinvertebrate classification, fieldwork protocols, and so much more with my scientists. In the last year, I have also integrated place-based studies and Indigenous knowledge and culture.

> A special note about incorporating Indigenous knowledge and culture within your curriculum: It is an honor to do so and a privilege to have this wisdom shared with you as a human being. If you have the opportunity to learn from elders and Indigenous leaders, please remember that knowledge and wisdom is sacred and should be regarded and passed on to others as such, always with explicit permission granted from the leaders who provided you with the gift of this knowledge.

With this project, students begin with trout eggs and raise them until the fingerling stage. They are then released into the nearest available freshwater source. For my students, this source is four hours away. While this could be considered a challenge not worth working to overcome, it actually allows my students to experience the geographic regions of our state, which just so happens to be a major part of the fourth-grade standards. On an expedition to this release spot, students travel through four of the five geographic regions—tell me they won't remember *that* content! Most recently, I decided to transform this expedition into a weekend event, throughout which we would experience fieldwork of different varieties at every turn. The plan was to release our trout and collect macroinvertebrate samples as well as water quality readings. We would also complete a biodiversity survey of plants, insects, birds, and bats while staying in cabins in the George Washington National Forest. COVID-19 had other plans for the weekend of this expedition, and we have not had the opportunity to see it through—yet. Unfortunately, the spring 2021 expedition shares the same fate as 2020, but I won't give up. You might predict after reading this much in the book that very little will stand in the way of me making this happen at some point in the future, even if it means I do the expedition alone, document it with my 360 camera, and share it in the interim with my scientists through virtual reality.

Whether you take on Trout in the Classroom or have guppies, goldfish, betta, suckerfish, tetras, or any variety of fish in a classroom habitat, there are countless ways to integrate them into whatever your content standards demand of you. At the very least, you can use them as a way to empower students to take leadership roles in sustaining life, earning the opportunity to feed it, name it, and change the water in the aquarium. You can use live specimen as part of an award system at the very least. One thing I can guarantee is that fish will captivate your learners and, who knows, perhaps even inspire the next Dr. Sylvia Earle!

Plants

Whether it's an out-of-control spider plant taking over your classroom or seedlings you plant in an indoor or outdoor space, plants can be a less threatening way to introduce living things you can cultivate into your classroom setting.

While it may not be possible space-, equipment-, or money-wise to have a representative plant from all levels of taxonomic classification, you can certainly use basic representations of some of the major levels of classification. For example, with just two plants, you can cover vascular and nonvascular. If you want to step up your game a little, you can branch into different seeding types. For instance, having a spider plant, fern, tulip, and tomato plant allows you to have vascular plants that reproduce via plantlet (spider plant), spores (fern), bulb (tulip), and seeds (tomato). If you do not have space, equipment, patience, or money to support these types of endeavors, a single plant of your choice can work wonders for student empowerment, curiosity, and personal connection to content and skill standards. Just as with animals as class pets, plants can be used as direct connections to content and part of a reward system or classroom job to empower students. By having the livelihood of a plant or several plants in their hands, your students connect, have ownership, and use their power to influence the plant's life. This could segue into how-to papers (how to take care of plants), creative writing (what do plants do when humans are away?), persuasive writing (convince your teacher or family to get a plant of your choice), statistics (tracking the amount of water, time exposed to sunlight, dark, or artificial light, amount of fertilizer added and frequency, change over time [height, girth, shape and size of leaves, flowers, roots]), sustainable farming and cultivation practices, historic uses of farming or agriculture in your locality or globally, engineering of irrigation systems, or even experimentation with different plant needs and their effects over time. There is a lot we can dream up here; you just have to think differently and say yes.

Fifth-grade scientists researched keyhole gardens of Uganda, then planned and built their own model, complete with seeds to replicate traditional crops.

Full-grown keyhole garden.

So, how will you harness the power and intrigue that live specimens bring to your content? Don't worry, you do not have to commit to maintaining living specimens in your classroom. In fact, many schools have regulations against it, but you *can* investigate them within your campus and even your building. How can you turn shrieks of fear in the hallway when a colleague or student spots a spider or cockroach into a lesson or experience that will make your content memorable? Or what about that weird plant that is scaling the walls of the school building outside (or inside—even weirder and more intriguing!)

Two scientists investigate beetles in the laboratory.

EDUCATOR ASIDE

Josh Whitlinger

secondary science educator

It was my first year teaching, and there was a student whose performance and behavior in class was completely hit or miss. I came to understand that she had home-life situations that prevented her from being fully engaged in high school, and she moved frequently. Due to another move, she asked me if I would take care of her hamster for her. I promised her I would keep it in class and take it home for the summer. When I asked the hamster's name, she told me she hadn't taken the time to name it and that I could have the honor of choosing. I named him Chewbacca, as any normal *Star Wars*–loving science teacher would. That's when things changed.

Students weren't late to class anymore. They would drop by just to "check on Chewbacca." I came up with the rule that "Chewy" could get in the exercise ball if all the students finished their work. The students started helping each other so they could sit in their chairs and watch Chewy run around the edge of the classroom in a purple ball. Chewy also became the center of many (animal-safe) science experiments. For example, as a design experiment, the students were asked to make a boat out of recycled materials that would support the weight of Chewy in her plastic exercise ball. Interestingly enough, I was observed when the students were testing their designs, and I found it quite amusing to read in my administrator's professional write-up that the "class hamster was enlisted in science experiments to calculate buoyancy in oceanography."

One day, a student decided to figure out how to tell if Chewbacca was a boy or girl. I had no clue how to determine this, nor did I have intentions of even approaching the subject, but all of a sudden, this student proved to me that Chewy was, in fact, a female. Since she was basically a school celebrity at this point, we decided the name Chewbacca couldn't be thrown out the window; we just changed the spelling of her name to Chewie (with a heart over the *i*.)

Chewie went on to live with a student at the end of the year, but this was just the beginning of having nature invade my classroom. My next idea was to have a fish tank. Students who finished their work early, were having a rough day, or just needed a place to sit quietly could have "tank time" and watch the fish. Often students would walk in and check out the tank, even when I didn't teach them anymore, because they were having a bad day.

For various reasons, I decided to look for a position in a neighboring district, and luckily, I landed a job in a school that focused on well-rounded learners and experiences that connected students to the world around them. I started looking for other ideas, when Becky introduced me to the Trout in the Classroom program. The project would provide about 125 trout eggs that would be grown in the classroom then released into the wild. Perfect! The students were able to see life changing every day, as eggs with tiny red lines grew into swimming fish within several months. At the culmination of the project, the fish were released into their natural habitat.

What began as one tank in the back of the classroom soon grew into a school club (Tank Gang), with seven tanks around the school that the students maintained and two hatcheries. One hatchery was dedicated to the trout, and another was for guppies that the students would provide to other teachers to have tank time for their students. Throughout this experience, we saw things like life emerging, fungus attacks, and mutations, as one trout was born with two heads, and death. Death happened so much that we had a "death total" board and would take a moment to honor each time an egg was lost.

As it happened, our school was going through a transition in which we needed to find a short class/study hall that the teachers would need to fill. Not needing another lesson to prep and knowing that the project would only last two years, we came up with the idea to have the students complete "passion projects." We taught them how to pursue personal interests and guided them through the process, particularly those who were struggling.

One student in particular was really struggling with finding a project she could do right then that she felt would make her more successful tomorrow. She said, "There is nothing. I cannot do anything right now in eighth grade that would make me better prepared for a career. I want to be a veterinarian!" When I asked if she currently had any pets, she replied, "No." I encouraged her to start there. Rolling her eyes, she looked at me in total disbelief and said, "You mean to tell me that I can go get a guinea pig and bring it to class and take care of it every day and that could be my passion project?!" Without a beat, I responded, "Yeah, that sounds awesome!"

That afternoon, her mom called, echoing the same tone and disbelief as her daughter. I responded exactly the same to her. The next morning, the student rolled into the school with a cage, food, exercise wheel, and a guinea pig named Eugene. Eugene came out every day for forty minutes, and the student learned everything about him, from ways to recycle materials for bedding to proper diet and health care. Several months later, this budding veterinarian applied for the health and science academy high school and wrote essays about learning the anatomy of guinea pigs as a passion project. Not only was she accepted, but upon graduation, her application to college was to pursue veterinary sciences.

For years, these animals would grow and show the students how life happens every day. As a teacher, it wasn't any extra work for me, as I would assign students the responsibilities of taking care of the tanks and critters. For some students, they had never had the opportunity to care for an animal. For others, it was the thing they most looked forward to at school. For me, it was an opportunity to reach students who were unreachable. All it took was for me to say yes.

CHAPTER SEVEN

WORDS MATTER

With the word *kleptoparasitism* posted outside of the laboratory door, I eagerly await my scientists. I have a "password" all scientists must say before entering the laboratory each day. Because I teach kindergarten through grade five, I rotate which grade level content it will correspond with. When I taught all subjects, I would still use this concept of a password to enter my classroom. I would rotate which subject area the word came from, and my students would be excited each day to find out when the word would be used and what it was all about. While this seems a bit contrived and not at all authentic, it's not in the use of the word here, but when they experience the word in context, that the true power of the vocabulary comes to life. You see, students will not be told the definition at this point; they merely see and say the word for the first time. During class, they will experience the word, and that is when I connect the password to the concept. Better yet, I am hoping that when my scientists hear the word in context, *they* will make the connection to the password they said to enter the laboratory.

The password for this particular day, kleptoparasitism, is especially for these second-grade naturalists who are about to arrive. My scientists are going to be studying the behavior of endemic species of the Galapagos and practicing the skills of naturalists, a type of biologist who focuses on interactions of living things in specific areas. In this case, they will be using photographs, videos, and stories from my expedition to the Galapagos, where I fell in love with the specific type of biology naturalists practice. I knew it was the perfect opportunity to tap into students' natural curiosity and see where it would take us in the laboratory! Kleptoparasitism is a behavior displayed in the Galapagos by frigate birds; they steal the food of blue-footed boobies. I was fortunate to learn of this behavior, observe, and capture it via photos and videos while on expedition. Today, my scientists will learn about naturalists by practicing the skills of observation using my footage. My eventual plan is to expand this lesson to our campus, with my scientists selecting a location to study on campus and becoming the ecological experts of their selected area.

As my second graders see the unusually large word and struggle to decode it in order to gain access to the laboratory, questions flood in about what it is, what it means, and whether it is a word for *their* grade level? I dodge them like a professional ninja and begin showing my students a map of the Galapagos, the actual expedition map that depicts my travels, and pictures of marine iguanas. Who doesn't appreciate a good endemic reptile?

Before showing them a video of marine iguana behaviors, I introduce them to a special friend, Walter Perez. Walter is a naturalist in the Galapagos, and just before the video I took of marine iguana behavior, he had, seemingly by magic, perfectly predicted what I would see. You see, naturalists study behaviors and interactions within specific ecosystems. They do this so frequently and with such care that they can predict what will happen in a scene. I recall this interaction between myself and Walter with my students, and they beg to see the video. I purposefully do not tell them what will happen, though, so they are on the edge of their seats.

"OK, naturalists, we can watch the video. When we watch, what do we need to focus on? How are we going to truly become naturalists?" I ask them.

Their replies begin immediately in the form of shouts: "Everything," "The iguanas," "Anything interesting," "What we hear," "What we see" . . . . You get the picture—and so do they. They need to focus on all interactions.

We watch the clip, which is about two minutes long. When I took the video, I intended to record the aggressive, territorial behavior of marine iguanas. The time of my expedition was early mating season preparation, so males were beginning to display fabulous reds, yellows, and greens along their normally pitch-black bodies. They had also begun claiming territory and colony groups. Males claim space and friends within the colony, and to display their claims, they have an odd head nodding behavior toward one another. If other iguanas do not agree on territory or colony claims, they will advance toward each other and begin pushing one another, head to head. They sometimes resort to biting and even a little bloodshed, all for their right to certain locations and colonies of friends. You can see all of this in the video.

When the video ends, I ask my naturalists to share within their team the observations they recall, and I walk around to listen to their conversations. Before they really begin their team discussions, count-

Scan QR code to view the video I use.

less naturalists yell, "Can we watch it again?" Of course, I let them, but after the fourth viewing, I decline a fifth. I redirect them to talk with their naturalist teams. As I listen, I am astonished. My naturalists are sharing things like, "One marine iguana dove into the water," "A small lizard ran away from a big iguana," "There was a small lizard on the head of a large marine iguana," "A marine iguana snorted out water," "A crab crawled around the two iguanas fighting," and so on. This is

all what I had intended for them to gain from the experience.
is is better.

They take their role seriously, and they absolutely astonish me. Honestly, I do not believe all their observations, so we watch the video one more time, and they eagerly point out so many behavioral observations and interactions that I had no idea were even caught on camera. With their laundry list of observations, we segue into naming what they saw using the language of naturalists. The words *adaptation, archipelago, endemic, basalt,* and *evolution* are sprinkled into our conversations. My naturalists are so excited about their newfound knowledge and expertise that they decide to make a documentary film. They script it and "hire" me as the naturalist narrator, insisting I speak on film with an accent. They want to play the roles of marine iguanas in a colony in the archipelago. My naturalists provided me with a list of words I need to use, and they decide they will use their knowledge to display the behaviors of the iguanas. These naturalists become movie directors and "teach" me what to do as the guest naturalist in the film. This is student voice, choice, empowerment, and true engagement. What I love most about this experience is that my students want to be the iguanas and want me to do the job of the naturalist, but they make sure I have a script complete with the specific language of a naturalist.

CALL THEM BY THEIR NAMES

What happened in my classroom in the above instance came about as a result of careful and calculated use of vocabulary. My scientists take their work seriously because they are referred to as scientists or, more specifically here, naturalists. Not only does what I call them matter, but the words they use to describe their work and observations also matter. They use the passwords from each class in context, not because it's on a test—I actually do not use tests or quizzes in my laboratory at all—but because they know they are scientists and those are the words that go along with their role. They want to learn the vocabulary, and they use it consistently. No arm-twisting necessary—no bribing, no grades.

Beginning with the small step of calling your students "scientists" or a more specific type based on your unit of study is a small change that makes a huge difference. It empowers your students to fill that role and take it seriously. It pushes them to learn more vocabulary that is specific to their content and motivates them to use it in context. There is no fabrication or rote memorization of vocabulary; there is only exposure to a concept and a lead scientist (you) giving the concepts names. Authentic exposure.

Did you catch that the password to enter the laboratory that day was not even used in the class? My naturalists were so caught up in being naturalists with the marine iguana videos that "kleptoparasitism" had to wait until the next day. "True engagement, motivation, and excitement are a problem," said no teacher ever.

It should come as no surprise that the words you use and the words your students use matter. Are they using the science vocabulary you need or want them to be using in context? Do they understand it? Learning, using, and assessing students' use of science specific vocabulary does not have to feel like punishment. Students do not need to write vocabulary over and over in rainbow colors, they do not have to write them in alphabetical order, and no, they do not have to be on a test. In fact, you do not have to use traditional paper/pencil, multiple-choice, true/false, or essay tests to assess science at all. Let's just stick with science lexicon here, though.

See what I did there? I snuck in a word that you may or may not have known previously, but you used context clues to figure it out. It's possible that you grabbed your phone or computer to google "lexicon," but you know what I *did not* do? I did not write the word and definition there for you to read, copy, memorize, and repeat for an entire week of homework and small group center rotations.

What science are you studying with your students? What scientists complete that type of work in the real world? *That's* what you need to be referring to your students as. Better yet, can your scientists find out what specific type of scientists conduct the studies you are completing in class? That's a great challenge to set forth for your students. This also has potential for library media and technology integration. Most likely, there are several different types of scientists who complete the type of work you are doing with your students. That's even better. You can interchange what you call your students or specify it to each lesson based on what it is you are doing. Another thought here, what if your hook for the unit was the type of scientists they will be and their challenge is to figure out what types of things they will study and do in the laboratory? That's right, calling your classroom a "laboratory" is another small but powerful change you can make for your scientists. Now we're experimenting. (Get it?)

For example, anytime you study living things, your students are "biologists." More specifically, though, if they are learning how to classify living things, they can be "taxonomists." Are you using microscopes to view water samples? They are now "microbiologists." Are you focused on animals who live in the water? Congratulations, they are now "marine biologists." You can be as specific or general as you want. What matters is the simple change in lexicon.

Another small tweak in lexicon for science is how you incorporate vocabulary within the content. The days of having a vocabulary list to copy, memorize, and regurgitate need to be gone forever. Instead, using words in context as you and your students *discover* them is what makes them relevant and easier to commit to memory. It is possible that you initially learned a word because you memorized it, but without repeated exposure and use, it will not become a part of your long-term memory.

EDUCATOR ASIDE

Jennifer Burgin (@MrsJBurgin)
National Board Certified Teacher, Exemplary Project Educator
& Educator Explorer

Katherine Willet (@WilletKatie)
seventh-grade life science educator

Phil Coursey
instructional assistant educator

The words we use matter. When I was eight and at my final day of vacation bible school, our small group counselors were giving awards to each participant. At my turn, I was handed a sheet of decorative paper that said, "Jennifer—Most Enthusiastic!" I began to cry. "Jennifer, why are you crying?" one counselor asked. I told him that I knew the word enthusiastic, and I thought it meant hyper and crazy. I didn't feel that way about myself. My counselor listened to me, and when I was finished, he said, "Enthusiastic means 'to be filled with spirit!' and we carefully picked this word just for you, our most spirited camper." Well, that changed everything! I giggled and enthusiastically danced about. At this tender age, I learned that words matter.

My experience as an enthusiastic camper led me to become an elementary educator. One of my earlier teaching experiences with vocabulary was the spelling list, in which ten usually random words with little connection to what we were learning were thrust upon my second-grade class. We all despised the spelling list, even me. Once, I told my learners that I found spelling lists *asinine*, a word my dad had taught me to use on someone making unkind choices toward me that would render their mouths shut since it sounded so saucy! "What's asinine?" the learners asked me. The glaze from their eyes disappeared as they collectively looked up from their spelling tests. As an example, I shared that spelling tests, like umbrellas with holes, are asinine. "It's silly!" one learner blurted. We all giggled and went back to the asinine spelling test, and I saw some learners whispering the word to themselves, keeping tabs on it for later. Believe me, asinine showed up on the playground that day.

After this experience, I tried to liven spelling lists up with bonus words worth bonus points. I pulled words like *parallelogram* and *quadrilateral* from math and *governor* and *peninsula* from social studies. Get yourself a tissue when seven-year-olds try to spell peninsula; you will cry from laughing at the mistakes! The bonus words were a spelling failure. Most of my students were spelling these words wrong, and no bonus points were awarded. However, the children were happy and giggling to try out multisyllabic words in their speech. This attempt taught me something: young learners crave real and meaningful vocabulary and want to be entrusted with it. They want to be keepers of the knowledge usually reserved for teenagers and grown-ups.

This revelation was big to me. When we decide what words to give learners, we are also saying what we believe they are capable of understanding. This aligns with the pedagogy that we as educators hold learners to a high standard. That's likely something you've heard tossed around at a staff meeting or online forum, right? I believe one way to prove we hold learners to a high standard is by the words we invest in them.

I reached out to two amazing teachers and friends of mine in Arlington Public Schools to talk science vocabulary. Phil Coursey is an instructional assistant educator at Wakefield High School and supports science instruction with learners identified as having special education and English as a Second Language support needs. Katie Willet is a science teacher at Williamsburg Middle School, which has a sizable population of language learners, and co-teaches with an English as a Second Language educator to ensure all learners are accessing science experiences. It struck me how similar our thoughts were on teaching science vocabulary, despite the differences in our age groups.

"I think about how students acquire language a lot," Phil told me. "In high school, if a word is multisyllabic, a student might check out." He shared that by then students have learned to tune out vocabulary perceived as difficult or not relevant to them as a person. Phil notices that part of the reason science vocabulary can be difficult for all high school students, not just ones with learning and language hurdles, is because vocabulary is decided for the learners—what words matter, what definitions are right, when to speak them. There is a lack of choice.

Phil described a typical high school science vocabulary activity: An educator has a list of words for a unit that needs to be taught. The lists are given to students, and they are asked to define each word. Memorize them. Take an assessment. In this activity, students are denied the experience to say the word, hear it spoken correctly, and grapple with it in the community. It's solitary and sad. In contrast, Phil vibrantly described co-teaching vocabulary with student buy-in during a geology unit: The learners were reading about volcanic rock. They had a list of rocks they were supposed to learn, and instead of defining them on their own, learners were asked to talk about the rocks and share their current understanding. Had anyone heard of *pumice*? Yes! One girl used pumice during a pedicure. The pumice was full of holes, so Phil led a discussion about why pumice was so light, how the holes got there, and why it is good for exfoliating human skin. The student shared her experiences with pumice, how it felt, and why it was the right tool. Phil says, "Take what the kids have. Show them they have something to offer."

"I think a lot of science vocabulary is normalizing and relating it to real life," Katie told me. "Taking off the stigma helps students understand that this is casual, everyday language!"

Katie and her co-teacher, Susan Tucker, spend a lot of time teaching Latin prefixes and suffixes to their students. If a student knows that *photo* means "light," they can transcribe that to *photosynthesis* in her class as well as *photograph* in another class. Katie and Susan also spend time helping students find their preferred modalities and using that in creating experiences around vocabulary that ends with students sharing their ideas together. Sometimes a learner will draw what a vocabulary word means to them, while a peer group will act out the definition. Learners view each other's work, correct one another, and adapt their definitions. "I want to get them thinking in different ways, collaborating and correcting each other's misconceptions." Katie remembered introducing a unit that involved the word *taiga* and asking if anyone had a connection to this word. All the faces looked back at her confused except for one, a language learner from Russia. Katie asked if he had experience with taiga, and he replied, "Of course!" Everyone from where he was born knows taiga and that it means forest. "What kind of forest?" Katie asked him. From there, her learner described the forests of his homeland and became the taiga expert in the class.

I recognize my own beliefs in what Phil and Katie described. We can invite learners to share what they already know or misunderstand about vocabulary by inviting them into the process. From there, we empower them with strategies to make the learning experiences rich and meaningful. One way I do this with my elementary learners is by offering them words as a gift. In the spring of 2020, I was leading a geo-inquiry experience for my kindergarten class inspired by visiting the Chesapeake Bay. Our content expectations were to learn about water, specifically that it flows. We did this through examining our local watershed.

"Friends, we know that rainwater in Arlington flows where?"

"Into the watershed!" they cheered.

I asked where water went in its next steps: underground or in the sewers, into Four Mile Run, then the Potomac River, next the Chesapeake Bay, and finally the Atlantic Ocean. They were supposed to learn *flow*, but in our experiences, they also learned names of bodies of water and that in collaboration they are referred to as a *watershed*. They learned about the life in these bodies of water, focusing on the blue crab and how water flows more than itself sometimes, like microplastics, which cause problems. They learned that sometimes fishers are impacted by crab population declines and that hurts businesses. They talked about these concepts using words like *ghost pot*, *shad fish*, *pollution*, *seagrass*, *algae blooms*, and *expert*. That last word referred to them.

"Friends, did you know that it is likely you know more about the Chesapeake Bay than your parents? It is now your job to educate them as an expert!" *Collective Little Human Gasps*

Empowered with vocabulary and meaningful experiences, my kindergarten learners transformed into Chesapeake Bay *experts*, undaunted by multisyllabic words and eager to unwrap them.

CHAPTER EIGHT

VARIETY IS THE SPICE OF THE CLASSROOM

A nd now entering the ring . . . the one . . . the only . . . GAAAAAAAAASTROCNEEEEEEEEEEEMIUS!

Cue 1990s Jock Jams Music

I climb on top of a lab table and flex my calf muscles (gastrocnemius) with an obnoxious "Ahhh!" just like an overdramatic WWE wrestling character.

"You see that?" I ask, again with the deep dramatic wrestling character voice.

"That's the gastrocnemius signature move, THE SQUEEEEEZE! Soon, you all will know the wrath, the sweat, and tears of that squeeze in the arena!"

I jump down from the table into a dramatic squat and slowly arise, imitating The Rock with an eyebrow lift and epic gaze across the room.

"If you want to take me on, you will need a stage name, an epic move, and a dramatic entrance skit highlighting your own epic anatomical feature. Who's readyyyyy?" I follow up in that same voice.

"Yesssss, I'll be *gluteus maximus*!" one scientist shouts, and the entire laboratory explodes in laughter.

"I'm going to be *triceps* so I can squeeze you into my armpit!" another scientist adds.

Shouts of all different muscle names fill the laboratory, and excitement ensues as my scientists embark on a completely new project I have never done before. I do not know why or how it entered my mind, but it did only five minutes prior to my theatrics. It happened on the spot. It was something new that would spice up my unit on human body systems with fifth graders.

EVOLVING YOUR TEACHING

As a science teacher to multiple grade levels—kindergarten through grade five currently—my brain is constantly jumping disciplines, skill sets, and ability levels. Each year of my current fifteen years in education, I have taught a different combination of subjects and grade levels from pre-kindergarten to grade five, which has been a beautiful challenge and has allowed me to continue pushing boundaries and thinking differently about the experiences I plan for my scientists. The standards remain the same, but how I address them is a different game. Every year, every month, every week, every day, and every class is different. Even every scientist is different and requires different experiences to develop their skills.

I literally revisit lesson plans every day to add or modify a skill or concept that is part of each grade level and each individual class. Sometimes this tweaking happens in the moment; a spark ignites during an interaction with a scientist or entire class and, boom, plans change. That sounds preposterous, I know. I will admit I am an overachiever, but what I really am is interested in how far I can stretch students, especially in their exposure to scientific concepts and critical thinking. For example, when I first began composing the fourth-grade curriculum at my current school in 2013, I knew I wanted to include geology—rock types, rock cycle, and earth processes—but what I did not know at the time is that I would amend the curriculum to more closely mimic field geology, and in 2018, students would manipulate geologic surveys of our state to complete field reports, suggesting where to find the earliest samples of metamorphic rock in Virginia. With the helpful nudges of Next Generation Science Standards (NGSS), motivational and inspirational colleagues, and my drive to push the limits of what can be accomplished with young scientists in the science laboratory, I make, test, implement, and continually tweak big ideas like this on the daily.

This is no exaggeration. Had I stuck to the curriculum I created in 2013, my third-grade scientists would never have explored a cave system and completed a biodiversity survey, my fifth-grade scientists would never have planned and cultivated a traditional Ugandan style keyhole garden, my first-grade scientists would never have made their own field guide for insects on my school's campus, and we certainly would not have created and maintained blogs, podcasts, and social media accounts documenting our work in each grade level. My second-grade scientists would not know how to solder electrical

Fourth-grade scientists completed research to raise brook trout and, based on that research, begin building the habitat.

circuits, my third-grade scientists would not have learned how to make organic soap or bath bombs, my fifth-grade scientists would not have mummified chickens or created exercise videos, and my fourth-grade scientists would not have learned to overhead cast and fly fish.

We must commit to the creative process that allows us to think differently about our content in order to reach every learner every day and every year, and not shy away from tweaks as often as they are necessary. We do not have to use the same experiment, demonstration (do not even get me started with demos), diorama, and so forth year in and year out. The way you make your content accessible to your learners every single day matters. Maybe you can use similar experiences from class to class, year to year, but if your whole year is scripted and you subscribe to the thinking that it is good enough, it is truly reaching every single learner, or that is how education should be, then you need to take some time to reflect.

Example of Lesson Evolution

My school has a global focus, and in the elementary school, each grade level has a continent to which their classroom content is tied. Fifth grade has the continent of Africa, and every year, I evaluate and, when necessary, reimagine how I will tie science content to the continent of Africa. In my first year at the school, I connected to the ecology of Africa, mostly to big cats while my scientists seemed to know the most about them and had interest about their location within the continent. We looked at what makes a cat a cat and even created abstract models of cats with things like springs, sandpaper, and string. I was hoping they would catch on to the metaphor of these types of items and how they could be used to animate the traits of big cats—sandpaper for the ability of their foot pads to grip and shear the ground below them as they ran, a spring to illustrate the flexibility of big cats and their spine—but it did not quite end up the way I had hoped. Those abstract connections were just out of reach for my learners.

The following year, I tied in our study of inventions and the creation of our own ideas to the study of Africa. What might we do, invent, or create that would be helpful to citizens of Africa or a particular country within the continent? I quickly realized, although already knee-deep in the study, how patronizing and white saviorist this project became. That was not my intention or vision at all, but that is what it ended up being; that was the project's final impact. I knew I did not want to have this type of impact again, so I began finding a new way to evolve my planning of African study within science.

The following year, I connected more to the geography and landscape of Africa, throwing my scientists into a situation to debate and ultimately make a decision upon. The scenario was that the government of several African countries wanted to build a highway that would connect the east coast of Africa to the west to improve trade relations, tourism, and a sense of community throughout the continent. My scientists took on different roles within different countries and the debate as a whole, representing different perspectives. My fourth year, their language arts classes took a specific focus upon ancient Egyptian mythology and culture. That year, to tie in human anatomy and ancient Egypt, we mummified chickens. From studying the practices both in methods and religious beliefs of mummification and its process, we immersed ourselves in the project by creating cartouches, sarcophaguses, and canopic jars, even tracing these methodologies over time to present day with localized embalming practices of the deceased. We learned a lot of anatomy and sociology of death through this project. We certainly learned a lot about how the mummification practice can go not as planned and how attention to details within the process greatly affects its success in preserving or exposing the decaying process of chickens. Nonetheless, our greater school community will not soon forget this culminating project and its associated smells.

My fifth year, we focused on agricultural practices of farmers and families in Uganda. My scientists researched local crops and local agricultural techniques, specifically keyhole gardens. To create their own replica, my scientists used math to figure out the largest possible circle they could construct within a square-shaped gardening area. Through this, they learned and reinforced math vocabulary for circles, radius, circumference, area, and diameter. They determined, based on measurement and calculations, how much material they would need to construct the garden walls and integrate a composting section. They researched typical African crops families cultivated and comparable crops we could grow here. It was a beautiful cross-curricular and global project that is still alive in our garden area today. Every year since, we have adopted a "think globally, act locally" mindset based on Jane Goodall's Roots and Shoots program.

In their general education classrooms, they study global practices in African countries, where local (to African countries) communities solve problems of global climate change, pollution, or other environmental challenges they face and connect locally (to us in Virginia Beach, VA) to environmental issues we self-identify. Through our invention study and creation to date, my fifth-grade scientists are tasked with identifying local issues to address through an invention of their own, creating an implementation plan, designing and prototyping a solution (invention) with a 3-D design printed on our school's 3-D printer, and pitching the invention, plan, and larger community rollout to a panel of local community experts *Shark Tank*-style. The project is titled "Dolphin Tank" because our school's mascot is a dolphin.

This year, still teaching through a pandemic, I am in person with many scientists along with learners tuning in live from home. I still have learners tuning in from home at the same time. This is certainly a challenge and requires me to think through and evolve this year's plans again to meet my learners where they are and deliver intended content and learning standards while also meeting their needs as in-person and hybrid learners. This year, I am also teaching exclusively outdoors, just another level of evolution, and keeping this year's project focus hyperlocalized. My scientists are focusing on our outdoor space, identifying problems to solve in our own learning space.

Do all of your units of study follow the same script? This is another area to weave in variety. There is something to be said for predictability, but this is also a major trap for monotony and outdated methods. One easy way to bring in some variety, if you have a little fear of disrupting your world, is to shuffle the order in which predictable components of your units are delivered. First, please think about your learners. Is the predictability factor of your unit and set of activities for their benefit or yours? Is it truly necessary to teach in the way that you are for your learners to best learn content? If you aren't sure, this is your cue to spice it up. If your answer is no, this is the bonk on the head you need to mix it up.

Think of it this way: you do not eat the same thing for every meal or watch a television or streaming series to see the same action every episode. Even on a show like *Queer Eye*, which has a predictable format, the content within that format varies based on the cast, the guest, the location, and the needs of the individual they visit. We can apply the same mindset to our pedagogy and planned experience for learners. Curriculum tells you the "what"; in *Queer Eye*, that would be the five men of the cast and their respective specialties. The experiences you plan for your learners is the "how." In the show, that would be the methods or activities each of the cast members utilize for the guest makeover. I do not recall in any episode of *Queer Eye* the same "how" being used by a cast member to achieve the results for their guest. Why, then, do we as educators accept this in our own craft?

Our curriculum seldom changes or changes only in minor ways. What should change are our methods, activities, and experiences, and these changes should be in direct response to our learners. There are so many ways to reach our destinations, to meet the demands of curriculum and content standards. Take advantage of that.

In 2019, I attended a professional development seminar with Dr. Angerina Jones as the facilitator, where I learned important strategies that have been proven effective for students of color. This does not mean they only work for students of color; in fact, while especially important for cultivating active learners among students of color, they are helpful to all students. By using these strategies, no one is harmed or excluded and all benefit.

Below I present the strategies Dr. Jones shared and that I have since been intentional about implementing in my classroom.

Movement and Kinesthetic

Dr. Jones eloquently described moving as being "in the blood" of Black and African American culture, so to speak. In order to be their best, Black and African American students need freedom to move, which can be provided via flexible seating arrangements, frequent movement breaks, or loosening your expectations of students being perfectly still, quiet, and seated in traditional chairs and desks.

With my young scientists, I allow free movement and access to equipment within the classroom. The materials I anticipate they will need are already organized in an easily located space, but I do not have them at their workspaces automatically. This accomplishes a few goals—movement, student agency, and fewer distractions as they enter. When materials are already at their workstations when they enter, students are tempted to go ahead and touch them without figuring out the goal of the experience for the day. This also, in my mind, tells my scientists, "I know what you need to do and what you need, so just wait for me to tell you everything." It places me at the center of the learning and experience, rather than them. Having materials around the workspace gives them an idea of what they might need or use for the experience but also allows them to choose what to get and, again, forces them to move around the room, naturally attending to that basic need.

Imagination and Humor

How can we re-imagine content to include aspects of creative thinking, humor, and imagination? Can you begin your lesson with a related comic on the board? Something to grab their attention, hook interest, and get them thinking?

To weave in imagination, creativity, and critical thinking, I often place my scientists in the role of meme generators, requiring them to think differently about content and connect to pop culture. Here are some we have generated together:

And then there is the matter of visual notetaking, where we incorporate humor to understand concepts, such as coral reproduction and global climate change.

You better believe with "It's getting hot in here" we incorporate some singing and dancing as well. I believe the exact lyrics we created on the spot were, "It's getting hot in here, 'cause global climate change. It is getting so hot with all those greenhouse gases." (Bonus points if you just sang that in your head with Nelly at the beginning and higher vocals on the second part; I know I did as I wrote it.)

Physical Action-Oriented; Learn by Doing

The best way to learn skills and continue to practice them is to just plain do authentic tasks. In what areas of your content do you feel the least "learning by doing" occurs? Experiencing the content, doing science, not just sitting back and passively receiving it, is the foundation of how I believe science content could and absolutely should be taught. It turns out this is a necessary strategy for historically marginalized communities, such as Black, Indigenous, People of Color (BIPoC) learners, and is engaging for all demographics.

If I want my second-grade scientists to understand atmospheric science, weather patterns, and forecasting, then wouldn't I have them use data to create a five-day forecast for our local area? Better yet, why wouldn't we use a green screen and deliver the forecast just as meteorologists do daily? Authentic practice of skills, that's it right there. A few years ago, I wrote a grant proposal to our parents' association to purchase a weather station, green screen, and microphone so my scientists could forecast. We connect with local news and weather stations to study and learn with meteorologists currently in the field. My scientists get to know data, what it means, how it is used to predict patterns, and how the puzzle is put together into a live forecast. As they learn about the data, they also learn about the tools of weather forecasting and deploy them. There is not a moment during the unit where I explicitly explain vocabulary, tools, or forecasting methods. We just do it, and we do it together.

Relationship Oriented, People Focused

"Relationships are king" is one of my all-time favorite quotes by CJ Reynolds, a high school English teacher and author of *Teach Your Class Off*. If we aren't connected to our learners and they do not feel connected to us, we are failing to serve a basic human need, no matter the demographics of our classroom. How can we make our science content relationship-oriented? What about when authentic tasks are being completed? How can we foster teams, collaborative groupings, and even cooperative learning strategies?

When I work in the field, collaboration is how we can accomplish data collection each day in a limited number of hours on site. We rely and focus on the relationships we have with one another and divide our work accordingly. In fact, prior to heading into the Peruvian Amazon, our team takes at least a day to just be together. We create plans, get to know one another, and soak in Peruvian culture together. This is the foundation for our work while at base camp. Trust, connection, and understanding are important when working with a short time frame, a to-do list the size of a buttress root, and safety concerns. Turns out these principles of relationship-based fieldwork are also paramount to the success of our Black and African American students.

Cooperative Learning

Cooperative learning strategies naturally incorporate movement and relationship-building, so no wonder it is an effective strategy for our Black and African American scientists. In my working space, whether in the laboratory or in our outdoor field station, I use cooperative learning as a communication tool. An important part of science is sharing results, analyses, conclusions, and next steps. This also happens to be a majorly neglected part of science as a whole in the academic years. I use Kagan Structures like Mix-Pair-Share and Stand Up, Hand Up, Pair Up to facilitate communication, interpersonal skills, and movement with my scientists. This is also a great opportunity to formatively assess learning that is happening without being invasive.

Beginning in March 2020, the world of education was spun on its head, shaken like a salt shaker, then like a snow globe, patted like a nearly empty ketchup container, and even wrenched and twisted like a super saturated rag you are trying to squeeze the last drop of water from before tossing it in the washing machine. The COVID-19 pandemic has presented quite an opportunity to use a variety of resources, platforms, new ideas, hybrids, and remixes of ideas. As we were thrust into a remote learning environment, we learned a lot. I know I learned a lot about what would not work online and, from there, realized what I *could* do—what variety I would be able to and must weave into my scientists' experience to find success, engagement, and our final destinations. Every day this opportunity exists; we just have to take it and run with it. Believe me, every day, I am not this excited, optimistic, or ready to take on the world. In fact, I will tell you there were several days in the summer of 2020 that expletives streamed from my mouth like a fire hose. In fact, earlier today, I was catching up with Adam Welcome on the phone and off went the fire hose of expletives. (Sorry, Adam!) But here I am only a couple hours later, with renewed hope, optimism, and gusto to infuse variety into our workspaces. You might stumble along the way, and you might rely on an "oldie but goodie." That's OK; I do, too. You will have days where you feel like, "What's it all for?" or you are so tired you give yourself a pass. That's OK, too. But promise me that the next day, you'll be back at it, looking for improvement, the best way to reach your learners, and that extra dash of spice for your students.

EDUCATOR ASIDE

Judith Painter (@JPainterGeog)
middle-school world geography educator and
Educator Explorer, intersectingpaths.home.blog

Teaching—good teaching—has a different look and feel between classrooms and years. Over the years, my classroom has slowly become a flexible seating arrangement. However, as I write this, I've had to dismantle everything to follow COVID-19 procedures; I still want my students to learn collaboratively and communicate with each other daily. Thus, this year will have me actively searching for and tweaking online and in-person collaborations within our guidelines. As an effective teacher, I have to be willing to make changes based on circumstances and even students.

Those changes come year to year. For several years, I had students learning about culture through mini-lessons on a topic, such as religion, language, and housing. Then, the students would work alone or in partner groups based on student choice to create their own country using geographic concepts and cultural information. The students loved the activity and learned some. However, in the past three years, I have found other ways to enhance the cultural unit with the result of more students remembering the information. Adapting and being willing to change as students and groups change is essential. Last year, I had one class of eleven with three ELA students who were reading on a K–2 level. In the same class, I had students in advanced English classes. I was able to build a community in the classroom of collaboration and support, which was quite different from my other classes. That class had different testing styles, but the results were the same in comprehension.

Another class had twenty-nine students in a collaborative classroom with an aide. Using similar collaboration and communication styles, I was able to group the students to work and support each other, using not just my classroom but the classroom that was empty across the hall as well as the hallways. In setting up the expectations for the activity, each student knew their responsibilities. Will I have a class of eleven and one of twenty-nine next year? Probably. Will I end up teaching them differently than last year? Most likely, as they will be different students in different mixes with different needs!

My school has three geography teachers, and all three of us teach with different styles and at different paces. Instead of our administration forcing us to conform, we have been encouraged to learn from each other but adapt lessons to our style. In turn, that gives our administrators a variety of choice when placing students who have had "bumps" in their learning. A student needing more structure would go to one of my colleagues, while a student needing more flexibility or exposure to nature might be placed in my classroom. In the past I have been told that a certain student needs more support due to this or that from seventh grade or from home. My teaching style allows me the flexibility to meet the student where they are and support them where they are until they are able to move forward without the scaffolding. On the other hand, I had a student in class two years ago who we decided would be more successful in a very structured classroom. That student soared in the colleague's class. By teachers working together to use their strengths, we can help *all* of our students be successful. By teachers not feeling inadequate if a student truly would be better with a colleague, we will be more willing to help and support our colleagues and students.

I leave you with a question: does all learning have to be inside your classroom walls? Consider the ways you can enhance your curriculum by using the world outside the four walls. Last year, a colleague and I wrote a grant to get our students outside and hiking. We took all of our students hiking and taught them how to use Rocketbooks, GPS units, iNaturalist, and Seek by iNaturalist. In one day of hiking, I saw more collaboration, learning, and sharing of student knowledge than I had in two weeks of desk learning. But what if you cannot find a grant or take the students on a field trip? Consider using simple observation of the outside world around your school. What can they find (use the five senses)? Could you start a small garden plot? What can they observe at home over the weekend?

So, as you continue your journey, consider two to three features you could use next week or month or even in the next unit to support your students in a new way. Every summer, I find a few new ideas I select to implement in the upcoming year. Do they all find a home in my classroom? No. Sometimes I try something and realize it will not work well with that group of students. Other times, the new idea finds a home and gets tweaked over the years. Be flexible enough that even a new idea over a weekend or long break could change you for the next unit. Once you know your students, you will know what you can implement on the fly and what will need more fleshing out.

I wish you the best on your continued journey.

CHAPTER NINE

LIMITED RESOURCES, CHALLENGE ACCEPTED

Winds sweep through the open doorways and windows. Papers crunch loudly along their edges from underneath rocks, binders, paperweights, and books that hold them as secure as possible. Clotheslines hang on the walls, secured with nails and heavy-duty packing tape. Anchor charts made of thick poster and foam board are hot glued to the walls to keep from blowing away in the seemingly permanent breeze through the schoolroom. It's clear that the rooms are designed to use the breezes as natural air conditioning and ventilation; educators and students alike accustomed to this type of air movement are unphased by the sound of rustling paper. They instinctively catch and brace papers down when the hint of a breeze erupts; they do not even seem to notice their own automatic behavior. Other than paper, school supplies are sparse here in Belmopan, Belize, but the rock star educators do not allow that to hold them back from providing the best education possible for their learners.

I'm here as an ambassador and instructional coach from the United States with Limited Resource Teacher Training (LRTT). I'm very much interested in what science instruction looks like here and am ready to pounce on any opportunity to engage with the students of my in-country partner educators. It will come as no surprise that reading and mathematics are the major educational priorities here in Belize, mirroring our own educational system in the United States.

It's S.T.E.A.M. challenge time, and it is my turn to take over the class to model practices that are easily adaptable to any situation, with no manipulatives, no supplies, no resources—and I am not about to use the paper they hold so precious for things like writing and illustrating for a science lesson.

I noticed earlier that all along the school's campus are large clumps of tall grass. Eureka! We are going to use that to create the tallest tower possible and integrate as many subjects as I possibly can to help provide a different perspective for my partner educators in approaching skills and educational standards.

I gather the Standard 2 class together; this is roughly the equivalent to first grade here in the United States. We are positioned perfectly next to a large clump of tall, sturdy grass. I am silent as I pick some of the stalks and begin weaving a hat for myself, complete with a large piece that sticks straight up like a tower. The students look on in wonder, I am certain, thinking to themselves, *What is Miss doing?* "Miss" is how they commonly refer to women educators in my assigned school. Some students begin giggling as they watch me using the grass to build something strange and place it on my head.

"I wonder which engineer can build the tallest tower hat?" I finally ask out loud.

They immediately rise to their feet and begin running around the schoolyard.

Oh boy, I think.

Dramatically, I stand up and exclaim, "WAAAAAIT, come back, engineers!"

They laugh and run back to me and sit down, hands full of grass stalks.

"I forgot to tell you—we need to draw our ideas *first*, then we will collect our grass."

Eagerly, the students laugh, look around at each other blushing, and attempt to hide their grass bounty behind their backs.

We use sticks to draw our ideas in the dirt, writing our names under our sketches. This is actually *way* more fun than engineering journals back in the United States. Each engineer stands proudly by their sketch and shows it off to their friends. We gather once more on the ground and I tell them, "OK, I am going to time you for one minute. You can gather as much grass as you can to build your tower hat, deal?"

"Deal!" they yell almost in unison and begin running to collect grass stalks, laughing almost the entire time. Their giggles and genuine joy are a melodic symphony accompanied by the smell of freshly cut grass and exposed earth (that they are plucking from the ground) and birds singing in the trees around the school grounds.

Perfect.

After collecting their grass stalks, they begin building, testing, modifying, and rebuilding until their hats are just the way they want them. As they modify their creations, they use their sticks to make new drawings, labeling them with numbers to show the different versions of their idea and what they are actually able to build. They resemble graphic novels in the dirt, illustrating their process and sequence of modification on the way. My mind wanders with ideas to use this type of illustration for sequencing in language arts, investigating elapsed time in math, and writing captions to practice nonfiction writing techniques.

Before I know it, the time to display our creations is upon us. An important part of science, which is often forgotten, is sharing and communication. I do not want this moment to pass us by.

"Can we walk in a parade line?" one engineer asks, interrupting my thought cloud.

"Of course we can!" I respond, and they instinctively line up behind me. As we parade the schoolyard, I shout to their teacher,

"What measuring tools do we have?" He shakes his head and I begin thinking, *What are we going to do?*

What did ancient civilizations do?

I got it.

I gather all of the engineers by the outside brick wall of the schoolroom. I set my hat on the ground, lick my finger, run it through dirt on the ground, and use the mud I created on my finger to mark the hat's height. I write my initials next to the line then motion for the next engineer to come up to the wall. As soon as one engineer walks up, they all rush, shoulder to shoulder and begin measuring their hats, marking with our homemade mud, and labeling with their initials. What's more exciting than writing on the wall with mud you made with your own spit? Yeah, I don't know, either.

Teachers begin rushing to the scene, looks of discontent covering their faces, and I prepare for the worst.

"This will be gone with the next rain, it's OK . . . it's science," I stammer. I was honestly afraid I had just committed a cultural faux pas, fearing I would be relieved of my position as an instructional coach immediately. They do not comment out loud, but their faces relax, and they begin to giggle and nod approvingly.

The bell soon sounds for snack time and the engineers instinctively take off for their free time. As they enjoy their snacks, they bring siblings and friends to the wall to show off their work. It's not quite finished, but they are proud. They did science—and we used none of their precious and limited school supplies.

EXPERIMENTING WITH WHAT YOU HAVE

What do you do when you do not have funding, resources, and manipulatives to teach science?

You persevere, you find a way, and you make it work. That's what I did, and that's exactly what those teachers in Belmopan do every day for all subjects. Instead of worrying about what you *don't* have, think about what you *do* have. A simple switch in mindset and metacognition works wonders. It's not acceptable to use the excuses of no money, no resources, and no time. You *can* teach science without fancy or expensive supplies or even with limited supplies.

Some of the greatest scientific accomplishments and foundational understandings were completed without modern-day technology, advancements, and knowledge. What you need is already inside *you* and your learners. Sometimes you just need to take a moment to think differently, reflect, and problem-solve. I found this extremely important during the COVID-19 outbreak that began for my state in March 2020. My school and community were incredibly fortunate to have a head of school that, for lack of a better phrase, saw this coming almost a month prior to the major changes that shook the education world to its core. I am incredibly thankful for his foresight, which made a major impact on how we were able to effectively begin to implement successful remote learning opportunities. Even with his incredible ability to predict and prepare for the possibility of this type of remote learning situation, it was still us educators who were left with creating the learning experiences necessary for our students.

First and foremost, it was and always is "relationships first" for me. Speaking directly to content, however, I can tell you it took me some real thinking to get to what I would do for my students with this new situation. As you've read, I pride myself on creating experiences and involving even the youngest of learners in field and expedition science opportunities. Immersing yourself in any content or skill is the way you learn best and most effectively. So what did I do when everything shifted to an online platform with limited synchronous time together?

I had an opportunity to go into my laboratory and bring supplies home, but I didn't. You do not need special materials or specialized equipment to do science. Also, my scientists at home wouldn't be privy to anything "special." Instead I decided I would take the opportunity to prove a point: science can and does happen everywhere, all the time, regardless of what equipment you have available.

What *do* we have at home that can help us investigate? My fourth graders were about to begin a unit on force, motion, and energy, a unit I typically begin with free exploration of Hot Wheels tracks and cars in the laboratory. I knew, however, that not all students would have this equipment at home. So then, what shall we do? What do I have in my own home? I found a marble and decided to create a marble roller coaster out of some of the most common items I could think of. I used a curtain rod, pillows, a small Nerf ball, books, and most important, gravity! I set up a track I thought would work, though it took me nearly twenty test runs before it actually did. The entire time, I videotaped the process, which would serve as a model to help hesitant scientists feel confident to explore in their own homes and provide a real example to demonstrate how what they were going to do would take more than one attempt to find success. I left the investigation open-ended for my scientists to use whatever materials they wanted—literally anything goes. I did make sure they knew they would need to consult whomever takes care of them at home as they worked to make sure they had permission to use the materials they wanted, but other than that, it was open source. I did not want anyone to worry about what they did or did not have at home, and I wanted to see their creativity and design process come to life. Being *this* flexible is something I will continue when we return to in-person classes. My style is already pretty open-ended and flexible, but I often place restrictions that can be unnecessary. Transitioning to remote learning, this new realm of having limited resources, taught me this about myself, my habit of unnecessary restrictions, and allowed me to reflect and improve my craft.

Common and Low-Cost Items That Can Be Used for Hands-On Science, Whether In Person, Hybrid, or at Home:

- LEGOs: can be used to build literally anything from chemical compound models to robots
- Marbles, tennis balls, baseballs, Wiffle balls, any type of sphere, really: to demonstrate laws of motion, for engineers to build "mazes" for the sphere to follow
- Paper clips: holding things together, as hinges for model construction, flags for labels
- Paper of any variety (tissue, notebook, wrapping, newspaper, magazine, packaging from a gadget)
- Cardboard
- Any table, chair, or stool: can be a workstation or way to produce and model potential energy
- Toilet paper or paper towel rolls: props, mazes for spheres, binoculars, tree models
- Milk or juice cartons from the lunchroom (or home): any type or enclosure you need, greenhouse, plant pot, small room for a circuit to light up
- Anything can be used for science, you might just need to think a little differently, or perhaps as Hiro in the movie *Big Hero 6*, hang upside down while your big brother shakes you! I actually use this clip to demonstrate to my young engineers how many tries it can take to "get an idea" or even begin.

Take this opportunity, this challenge, to think differently about what you *do* have rather than what you *don't*. This is going to be especially important as we transition back to in-person instruction. There will be restrictions and constraints in place that we will have to find ways to work within. That's just it. We have to see them as challenges, obstacles we can work to overcome rather than excuses to rely on outdated, and dare I say, boring options. Whether it is rethinking how to work a cooperative learning strategy while maintaining physical distancing protocols or using a different type of learning material or location, we must persevere and continue to find ways to make education, especially science education, the best it possibly can be.

EDUCATOR ASIDE

Chris Anderson (@TheScienceJedi, @sciaroundcincy)
instructional coach, host, and executive producer of *Science Around Cincy*

When I was seven, my dad took me to see the original *Jurassic Park* in theaters. Like so many kids of my generation, I was enthralled with what I saw: dinosaurs so real it felt like they made the movie with actual living creatures. While I may have missed the finer plot points, one thing I took away from the movie, beyond my newfound love of dinos, was that *life finds a way*. It's a phrase easy enough for children to understand that sums up much of what the film is about: that success, both in evolution and in life, is so often determined by one's ability to persevere in seemingly impossible situations.

Teaching science is challenging no matter where you are, but even more so in schools with limited resources. I've spent most of my career in these places, where glassware or lab time must be shared between teachers or the budget for consumables is whatever I can afford out of pocket. And field trips? District money for those got cut a long time ago. How can we properly teach science without equipment or materials for students to explore and experiment in the world around them? Teaching science without the hands-on experience of a lab is like a world without Bruce Springsteen: you can live in it, but would you want to?

We cannot relegate ourselves to boring PowerPoints and bookwork. Science, after all, is based on asking questions that don't have a seemingly obvious answer. Researchers don't spend years collecting data to answer multiple-choice questions. We do, however, have a secret weapon:

critical thinking and problem-solving. The central tenets of science need no supplemental materials to develop. All you need are young minds, which, as luck would have it, are delivered to your room every day, free of charge.

Observation, the first step in the scientific method, is also one of the best ways to engage your kids. Video clips that show the strangest and coolest scientific phenomena from around the world are free to access and can be shared easily. Students, especially teenagers, love what is taboo. Use the wild and weird to engage your kids and develop their observational skills. Demos are great ways to show concepts in real life, especially if you don't have quite enough materials for all students. And nearly every child has a supercomputer in their pocket connected to the entire wealth of human knowledge in the form of their smartphone. Can we take what is normally a distraction and turn it into a way to spark curiosity?

But observing phenomena is just the start of the scientific process. Delving deeper and asking why is necessary to get kids to think. Asking your students questions, soliciting their opinions, and fostering discussion can all be done at bargain prices. And not only are these strategies cheap, but they are also necessary for pushing students into the higher levels of Bloom's taxonomy.

No matter how great your discussions are, students still need hands-on, inquiry-based lessons to give them mastery of science concepts. In schools with limited budgets and resources, this is no doubt a big hurdle for teachers. But you don't necessarily need extra equipment or technology. What is crucial is providing students with an environment to try, fail, and learn. Some of the best STEM lessons I've seen were done with basic materials like string, plastic straws, and construction paper. It takes extra effort and curiosity to provide kids with opportunities to inquire, explore, and learn. But isn't that what we so often ask of our students? Shouldn't we lead by example and find innovative solutions for our instruction?

In a just world, teachers wouldn't even have to ask for the supplies they need to make their classrooms the best place on the planet to learn.

Your job is hard enough without having to beg, borrow, and steal to foster a learning environment. And we shouldn't stop fighting for the day when schools are palaces and educators are celebrated as the heroes they are. But we can't turn a lack of resources into a crutch that prevents us from providing deep, rich lessons for our kids. No matter what tools we do or do not have at our disposal, we always have young minds who are yearning to be challenged. We can and must do better.

In *Jurassic Park*, life finds a way. You can, too.

CHAPTER TEN

STEM/STEAM

"Eye of the Tiger" plays
Dun
Dun dun dun
Dun dun dun
Dun dun duuuuun

As my scientists line up in the hallway, I raise the volume even louder, don my lab coat like a boxer's warm-up robe, and trot to the door in my best impression of professional boxers in the ring.

"Aw, yeeeeeah!" one scientist exclaims.

"It's on!" another adds.

"It's bracket time!" a third announces.

They rush the laboratory like the fans of a national championship–winning team. With their thumb models in hand, my learners gather around a central lab table to build the bracket. All of my scientists' names are in a beaker (what else would you use in a laboratory), ready to be pulled. With the brackets determined, the entire class surrounds the "ring," cheering loudly, and I serve as the referee for this single-elimination thumb war tournament. Every battle is recorded with an iPad. It is epic to say the least and highlights the best of rigor, relevance, engagement, and student voice and choice all within one STEM challenge.

Part of my fifth-grade curriculum is human body systems, and each year, I look for ways to up the ante for my students. My intention with this STEM challenge was merely to have students use the engineering and design process to create an articulated model of the thumb with accurate movement. They had previously used the engineering and design process to create a leg model with muscles, bones, and tendons, which served as a great warm-up. In fact, my students became very comfortable with the process and relished the opportunity to show off their final creations, update their design sketches, and think of ways they could continue to improve from that point. One scientist even suggested I order more materials so they could create a complete hand model.

Wait, what?!

This got my wheels spinning, and I immediately jumped on Amazon with him to scope out the prices and see what we could do with his idea. As engineers continued to come to me, flexing and extending their phalange models, my mind jumped to thumb wars. This thought was really the result of one eager engineer shoving her creation into my face out of excitement. In that exact moment, it reminded me of the game we all play: thumb wars. I immediately grabbed my articulated thumb model and attempted a phalange war with her. Everyone around us began to cheer.

Yes, that was it. We *would* battle. This is nearly an exact quote of what I said in the midst of the phalange coliseum of scientists that was now constructed: "Oh my gosh, what if we made a bracket and had a tournament. Who's in?" The crowd went wild. They were definitely in. I hurriedly wrote a note for myself to construct the bracket outline for the next day. They all had to take their creations apart and head to Spanish. As we were all picking up the pieces of our models, I started thinking about a playlist that would be the background for our tournament: "We Will Rock You" by Queen, "Final Countdown" by Europe,

"Eye of the Tiger" by Survivor, "Welcome to the Jungle" by Guns N' Roses, "Sandstorm" by Darude, and "Let's Get Ready to Rumble Remix" from Jock Jams.

Scan the QR code for the playlist if you are curious.

The next day we began reconstructing our models as I blasted the playlist. Just as we made a little headway on our models, it happened. A fire drill. Seriously? On Phalange War Day?

After completing the drill and rushing back for the tournament, we resigned ourselves to calling it a practice day and making the official tournament the following day. This gave us time to come up with tournament rules and protocols. I listened and watched as they formulated their ideas and came to a consensus about how the tournament would play out. This was a wildly successful addition to our skeletal and muscular system study, and the credit goes to my students.

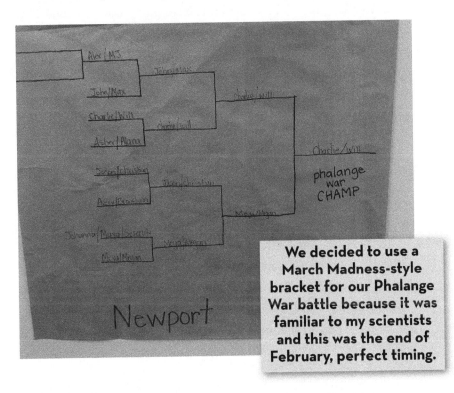

We decided to use a March Madness-style bracket for our Phalange War battle because it was familiar to my scientists and this was the end of February, perfect timing.

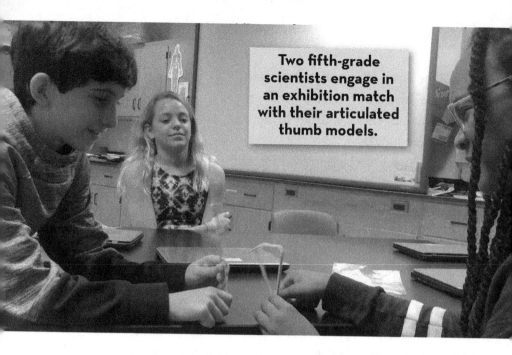

Two fifth-grade scientists engage in an exhibition match with their articulated thumb models.

KEEPING THE E IN STEM/STEAM

Love it or hate it, STEM and STEAM are going nowhere, and they shouldn't. If you break STEM and STEAM down, they are just good teaching. It's cross-curricular, involves critical thinking and problem-solving, and it's how we should always be teaching.

There are variations on the acronym out there, but it most commonly breaks down as:

Science

Technology

Engineering

Art or sometimes architecture

Mathematics

In the education world, a lot of ideas parade as STEM and STEAM, and it's about time we confront that. Just because you use math in science or science in math does not mean the work is STEM or STEAM. That would be called "SM" or "MS." That "E" is so incredibly important, though. For most educators, it is the least natural piece of STEM and STEAM. So let's focus there.

Engineering is a process. It involves planning, testing, and modifying ... followed by more and more of those pieces. It's a process, and it takes time; it can be frustrating and messy, and it is the single most neglected piece in STEM and STEAM. It's the piece that separates real STEM and STEAM from all the imitations.

If you create a model and just show it, it is not STEM or STEAM. Let's take a look at the articulated thumb model challenge I described at the start of this chapter. If I simply challenged my scientists to "make an articulated thumb model" or perhaps just "a thumb model," then provided the materials, they built them, and the project ended, that is not STEM or STEAM.

Before building, engineers need to plan what they will do, sketch, label, list, and so on before they access materials at all. OK, they can have the materials as they sketch and plan, but that is not the moment of actual construction. I tend to withhold materials during the planning phase to ensure that engineers are actually planning, sketching, and labeling, not getting knuckle-deep in the building phase without thinking first.

After planning, they then build and construct *based on their plan.* This is tricky because many young engineers will ignore their plan outright or decide to put it aside when the reality of construction does not match the plan. This takes discipline and a lot of practice, patience, and reminders from you, the lead learner. If they realize their plan is not going to work, they can certainly build something different, but they need to then update their sketch. Notice the word update—not erase, not throw away, not scribble out. They must update the sketch by adding a new one to keep track of the process. There's that word again: process. This is not a one-and-done. This is not a "quit when it doesn't work out on the first try." It is a process that can be frustrating and, dare I say, difficult?

After constructing the model, it's time to test. Does it do what it was meant to do? What can be improved about it? What needs to change?

Now it's time to think about the next step and sketch the modifications necessary. Yes, we are sketching and planning again *before* making adjustments. Then adjustments and modifications are made and tested again . . . then modifications, sketching, planning, building, testing, modifications, sketching, planning, building, testing, and around and around we go. Engineering is a process; it is not something you can complete quickly if you are staying true to the process.

Let's break down the articulated thumb challenge into the components of STEM and possibly extend into STEAM.

S The *science* component of this project was human anatomy, more specifically the functionality of the thumb as an articulated phalange.

T We used popsicle sticks, rubber connectors, string, and twist ties as our *technology* components in addition to iPads for documenting the process along the way. All of the photographs and videos that were taken were then assembled into a movie created by my learners.

E Throughout this two-week process, my scientists designed, sketched, planned, built, tested, and modified until tournament day. They kept an *engineering* journal filled with their notes, sketches, and reflections of the experience.

A *Art* could be arguably a part of this project since my scientists had to make the thumb model articulated and accurate in scale to the human thumb. I did not explicitly have this component in the project the first year we did it, although the following year I did. This is an easily added component of complexity to make the model look like an actual thumb.

M The mathematics component of this project came in the necessity of it being an accurately scaled model of a human thumb. They measured thumbs and ensured their models fit the appropriate measurements in order for their creation to be in accordance with the challenge and tournament guidelines.

Yes, this particular project took two weeks from start to finish. That's a lot of time for one small component of my human anatomy unit, but what did my students learn in that two-week time? A whole lot that crossed curricula and made them better thinkers, problem-solvers, and communicators as well. That's two weeks well spent.

Now this is where I run the risk of making a lot of people upset, but I am here for it: STEM/STEAM nights are not a thing. There, I said it.

I am willing to amend that sentence on one condition only; if your STEM or STEAM night contains the entire engineering process mentioned above, then sure, keep calling it STEM or STEAM. If not, go back to calling it Math and Science night. This is a difficult truth for many, and goodness knows there are many STEM or STEAM activities *sold* on the internet that do not meet the actual criteria. The real truth is STEAM and STEM are difficult and time-consuming.

I promise you, though, committing the time and effort to true STEM and STEAM is worth it and will yield incredible value to your learners, from the science and math content to communication skills and resilience-building. True STEM and STEAM are powerful and empowering, but it takes commitment to the entire process.

EDUCATOR ASIDE

Peg Keiner (@pegkeiner)
director of innovation and 2019 National Geographic Education Fellow

I have a complicated relationship with the word *artist.* As someone who did not have a formal art class until college, the identity of "artist" felt outrageously out of reach. It was a title I held on a pedestal piled with abstract paintings. Growing up learning how to program, I identified as a coder and a problem-solver, but it was not until adulthood that I learned the importance and power of art in our designed world. We are surrounded by nature, but we inhabit and consume our own designs, all of which are constrained by scientific phenomena. To foster divergent thinkers, we need to support students in developing a capacity for examining the world through layers of complexity and building confidence in their creativity as a flexible, stakeholder-centered problem-solver. In the same way a painting requires an audience to unravel its meaning, we must teach students to develop critical dispositions to analyze their own creations and the intricacies of the phenomena we choose to study. Seymour Papert's constructionism theory, the Carnegie Mellon CREATE Lab, and Agency by Design from Harvard's Project Zero have been instrumental in helping me form my mindset around STEAM integration in our curriculum.

In my interdisciplinary work in STEAM, art class is the path through which we explore phenomena. What scientific concepts are enmeshed in the process of taking a photo? Even the most basic of camera obscura creations will require examination into concepts of light, human anatomy, mirrors, and building materials. To design something new that solves a problem is to understand the "parts, purposes, and complexities" of the components. We use thinking routines from Agency by Design to unpack the parts and create sketches to see student learning. Their thinking routines are available for free online and are phenomenal tools for critical analysis.

Art is often a provocation before we begin a unit of inquiry on any topic. From Monet's haystacks to Georgia O'Keeffe's flowers, art makes us emotionally connect with nature and is a visual documentation of the influence it has had on humans. How might you use art to keep data on the weather or biodiversity? The "Dear Data" project by Giorgia Lupi and Stefanie Posavec is a favorite project I use as inspiration to both collect and communicate data. In the project, the designers use color and shape to create new beautiful ways of sharing information with each other. Science communication that is both aesthetically pleasing and clear has the storytelling power to inform people about their relationship to the vital data collected.

STEAM programs provide an opportunity for students to use technology, both low-tech and high-tech, as a material to express themselves.

Whether you are exploring algorithms and computational thinking through turtle drawing or using the raw materials of a Hummingbird circuit board to design a robot that meets your needs, a STEAM education provides access to open-ended resources that invite students to move through a reflective and intentional design within the constraints of the engineering design process.

During a storytelling unit of inquiry, students used STEAM components to code a robot character or scenes from a story they wrote. They were required to show knowledge of specific technology, art, and math skills to code their stories to life. Stories can also be used as inspiration for engineering design challenges. The CEEO Center at Tufts University created Novel Engineering, a program that invites teachers and students to select a problem from a story to solve through the engineering design cycle. Creating space for students' self-expression and creativity through STEAM will show them that these are tools they can use to power their own solutions. How could STEAM be a pathway to personal and community liberation? How could you use the cycle to creatively solve problems in your school?

Consider, as well, how you can make your STEAM program culturally and geographically relevant. Find out what issues matter to your students. During an environmental impact unit of inquiry, our students mapped out a plan to test air quality in our city. We partnered with our local Environmental Law and Policy Center to borrow air quality sensors to contribute missing data to their map, but students also researched their own locations and created an original model to communicate the information to the public. Their data revealed that a significant contributor to the pollution was a local business and their visual model communicated that to our nonprofit partner.

In the same class, another group was passionate about waste in the area and used the Marine Debris Tracker app to collect data on trash in our neighborhood. Reflecting on their findings, they were able to find out which part of the neighborhood was repeatedly impacted and found out cigarette butts were the primary debris. Students created and tested the impact of a visual campaign to target businesses and local neighbors to inform them of the issue. When students have an opportunity to design for an audience, they can test their designs through user testing. There are clear best practices in visual design and movie-making that guide students in creating powerful STEAM projects. How might you incorporate meaningful design challenges where students could test the impact of their designs through community engagement? Do you have a local community partner that could talk about how their designs impact the community?

Over the course of my own professional development as an educator, my identity has changed through STEAM, tinkering on personal and public designs. I have felt my confidence increase, and social media has been a platform to acquire critical feedback and see the reverberating effect of successful STEAM communication. In a world ruled by design, STEAM creates a pathway for the critical conversations needed to fully analyze and understand the power we have to empathetically and ethically design a complex world constrained by nature.

CHAPTER ELEVEN

VISUAL MEDIA

The smell of soil permeates my nose as I lie motionless in a side plank, tucked under the edge of a large, moss-covered rock outcrop in the middle of the Amazon rainforest. My head brushes up against the soft, cushion-like moss as I wedge my legs backward until the entirety of my posterior side is under the rock overhang and flush with the wall of rock underneath. I feel and hear juvenile tarantula nests ripping with my movement. I stop moving my legs. I do not want to permanently damage these nests, nor do I wish to have protective adult tarantulas making their way onto my legs or, even worse, up the inside of my pant legs. As I readjust my left arm, the one holding me up in a side plank, I am startled by the furious flight of bats that I have also disturbed here. I have invaded their homes.

"It's OK," I tell myself. "This is for science."

I set my phone in front of me and prepare to trigger the 360-degree camera that is on top of the rock under which I am hiding. My responsibility here in the Peruvian Amazon is to take 360-degree imagery that will serve as a way to track conservation efforts, natural changes, and human interaction within this area over time. With the images I capture, we will not only be able to track change over time for our own research, but we will be able to create virtual and augmented reality tours to bring the field experience to classrooms worldwide. Even better, I will be able to teach my scientists to use photography, both traditional stills and 360-degree images, to demonstrate concepts, capture the attention of audiences, and tell stories about scientific content.

After all, a picture is worth a thousand words, right?

––––––––

"Whooooooa." Excitement thunders from my scientists. Their chorus of engagement fills the laboratory with energy.

In my hand is my cell phone with the Google Expeditions app opened and the virtual reality tour I created for them of the Peruvian Amazon loaded and displayed on each of their devices. With every swipe on my screen, a new image appears, allowing them to experience the thick forestation of the Amazon. They rush to scroll around each image or spin in their chair to see their surroundings, call out questions, and call their friends' attention to things they observe. Four scientists take turns using VR goggles for an even more immersive effect. I have two Google Cardboards, one Merge headset I bought on my own, and one freebie sample of clip-on VR goggles I received from a screen printing company.

"Whoa, you can see tarantula webs on the rocks above your head, Mrs. Schnekser!" yells one scientist, as countless other voices cry out, "Wheeeeere?"

"Find Mrs. Schnekser and look above her head!" a scientist calls out, as a chorus of "Ewww, gross" and "That's so cool!" fill the laboratory.

Instant engagement.

This first round of exposure to this tour is completely open. I am in charge of swiping to the next scene, but other than that, my scientists control their view, exploration, and engagement with the foreign environment surrounding them. With every new scene, a chorus of "ooohs" and "ahhhs" can be heard halfway down the hall. The second round through the virtual tour, I take control of what they see, pointing their attention to embedded images and text I have made within the virtual reality tour to teach them about what they are seeing and experiencing. This is much like bringing them to a new location for the first time, an outdoor exploration, or field trip to a museum. I first let them explore on their own, then call their attention to things I know they need to experience.

With the power of virtual reality, I can bring my students literally anywhere in the world—even outer space.

I created my VR tours using Google's VR Tour Builder (arvr.google.com/tourcreator) and my own personal footage from the field, sharing with students via Google Expeditions app. In June 2021, the Google Expeditions app will cease to exist, meaning the ability to share self-created VR tours via the app will no longer be available. You will still be able to share those VR tours you find or create, just not with the convenience of the app and its teacher/guide control features. Premade VR tours and AR experiences will be available via the Google Arts and Culture app; we will simply lose the ability to share our own generated content in this meaningful way.

THE POWER OF VISUALS

Visual media, which includes photography, video, augmented, and virtual reality, is a powerful tool to bring into your classroom. Students nearly always engage immediately with visual media, and it has the potential to open endless doors. Let's explore a few ways these tools can be put to work, helping your learners participate in authentic, exciting science experiences.

Photography

Often, I begin a lesson by simply showing a photograph and asking my students to write everything they know or can observe in the picture. Take, for example, this photo.

Magnificent frigate bird flying above me in Galapagos on an overcast day.

The first thing my students write is probably what you thought: bird. Some students even put their pencils down after writing that word, but, of course, I don't let it end there. I say I have noticed more things that I will write down. Classic teacher move, right? Teacher Talk, this weird thing where we voice our thoughts out loud to help spark ideas for our students. My students begin adding words like clouds, white, beak, wings, tail. It's a great start, but they aren't off the hook yet.

My next questions are: What can you tell from this picture? What are some observations you can make about what you see? What do you know based on what you can see here?

This time, I let them make a list as a team and challenge them to make the longest list. They start writing things, like the bird is flying or the bird can fly; the bird might eat small bugs or fish; the weather might have been rainy.

Yes—now we're making some progress.

This is where we really dig in. We use the bird's anatomy, particularly its tail, to identify it as a magnificent frigate bird. This is a bird we had studied just before I left for the Galapagos, where I took this photograph, but the students don't immediately recognize it because they're used to identifying it by its red gular pouch, the iconic part captured in most photographs of these birds. From there, we move into a discussion of kleptoparasitism, which springs from my story of observing this frigate bird steal the food of a blue-footed booby (and many others attempting to but failing). This leads to talk of similarities and differences between the two species and, eventually, to climate change, competition for diminishing resources, the need for adaptation, and evolution. Whew. And that was all from one photograph.

A single photograph can evoke major conversation, exercise critical thinking and observation, begin a web of storytelling, and bring about deep connections to content without even trying. What photographs will you use to make your content come alive?

Let's take this one step further and consider how you can allow students to take photographs to illuminate content and become content creators. One really fun thing that I do with my students, and even myself, is using LEGO minifigures to create a scene.

Three LEGO minifigures in the sand of Isla Isabela, Galapagos.

Here, for example, is a shot I took in the Galapagos using these minifigures. Fun, right? But it's much more than that. LEGO minifigures are great for showing the scale of items in the field. In this photo, my figures helped me document grain size and color of the sand on each of the islands I visited, and they help my students really process what they are seeing. If I just show them a photograph of a leaf, for instance, they have no idea if it's smaller than my thumbnail or larger than my body. But with the LEGO minifigures, they can quickly grasp the scale.

With my young explorer scientists in the field, I teach them the art and skill of this type of documentation as well. It exercises photography, storytelling, scientific reasoning, and perspective skills and allows for a lot of content crossover. Often, I have my scientists complete short technical writing to go along with their photographs, but they could also be creative in writing about the scene. It does not have to strictly be science content; we can create fantasy writing pieces, miniature worlds, and *Honey, I Shrunk the Kids*-style pieces.

A LEGO minifigure next to an insect in the Peruvian Amazon to document scale.

For examples of how others use these LEGO minifigures to create scenes on location, search #legography on social media.

Video

Another way to engage students is through video content. I am not talking about canned videos you find on the internet or have on DVD; I'm talking about content you have created. This does not have to be a fancy Scorsese- or Lee-caliber creation. Often my videos are B-roll that I capture spontaneously, meaning there is no planned narration within the video. It might be a series of shots of my feet across different sediment types or of a Sally Lightfoot crab in the Galapagos retreating from a wave on the shoreline. Sometimes it is an improv narration by me on location, which can range from a faraway place to my own backyard. Regardless, the videos carry more meaning to my young scientists because I captured them. They are more connected to whatever happens because of their connection to me, the videographer.

Now, think about that for a moment; video I collect and share is more exciting to them because of our connection, that of lead scientist to scientist apprentice, if you will. What if we allowed our young scientists to be the videographers, documenting content they encounter? Their connection, understanding, and engagement with the content would be even stronger because they have been empowered to create that content. Think about it. How many times has one of your learners come to you beaming because of a connection they made outside of school to something you investigated together? All. The. Time.

I receive daily gifts of dead insects, bones, and stories about "something cool they found" at home. Our students cannot wait to share with us and bring us these little reminders and connections. Who knows, you also might have the next Spike Lee sitting there in your learning space. This might be the first time they realize a passion, take a chance, and make a connection that will forever change their lives.

Whether it is learning the secrets behind green screen video manipulation to create a weather forecast, creating a stop-motion animated video to capture the essence of what wildlife conservationists do, capturing a time lapse of butterflies emerging from their chrysalis, or just plain making video content without their audience experiencing vertigo, these are skills that will follow them into all aspects of life and inspire opportunities for your young scientists to express themselves in new ways.

Virtual and Augmented Reality

I understand that the idea of virtual reality can be daunting, that you might think you need expensive equipment that you don't, and may never, have. But that's not the case. I do not have a set of VR goggles in my classroom. Your students do not need them; the magic is not lost without VR headsets, I promise. I must confess that as I write this, I am in pursuit of acquiring funding for a class set of VR goggles, which will be awesome if I can secure, but you do not need to have them. I currently use school-issued Chromebooks and iPads as well as donated smartphones that would be recycled when the user chooses to upgrade their phone. My scientists scroll through the images within the tour on the Chromebook, iPad, or smartphone screen. With an iPad or discarded smartphone, they can physically rotate their bodies while holding the device in front of their face to view the images. If you don't have iPads, Chromebooks, or hand-me-down smartphones, you can use your teacher-issued computer connected to the classroom projector and view it as a class community.

Don't let a lack of high-end technology discourage you from trying virtual and augmented reality. See what you can do rather than what you can't. This is a great opportunity to connect with community partners; you might be able to find a local tech company, technology repair shop, or even equipment lending facility that will loan equipment like a library. Speaking of libraries, there are public libraries that have loaner sets of equipment. Maybe your local one does!

Virtual reality is an excellent way for students to complete biodiversity surveys and practice fieldwork skills prior to going on a field expedition or in place of a costly field trip. To date, I have had my scientists complete two such experiences. One of the projects was created by the United States Geological Survey (USGS) and called Project eTrout. For this project, my scientists viewed underwater 360-degree videos and were tasked with counting the number of brook trout they viewed in each video. The added complexity here is that there were other fish in the videos, so not only were my scientists tasked with careful observation for brook trout, they also had to distinguish between different species of fish within the immersive videos. For the second project, I used my own videos from the Galapagos and tasked my scientists with the challenge of counting the number of marine iguanas in each image I had collected from different islands in the archipelago. With this data and the use of virtual reality, they were further tasked with tracking species density throughout the archipelago. This is an incredible opportunity for our young scientists to connect to fieldwork while remaining in their home locations, which is especially exciting in the time of a global pandemic like we are experiencing as I write this chapter.

With augmented reality, my students can view, manipulate, and even pose for pictures "holding" objects they normally could never experience. While studying outer space and space exploration tools, my students can hold the solar system in their lap, spin planets to view them in their entirety, and count the moons orbiting each of them. They can go inside the International Space Station and even view our home planet, Earth, from a new perspective. They are able to manipulate comets, galaxies, and stars as well. We have even dabbled in taking photos of each other "holding" planets, which my students absolutely loved. A few groups even played around with placing planets and moons inside the fish tank, garnering giggles and sparking a few students to undertake some creative writing. Imagine how you could purposefully integrate writing with augmented reality. What if, for example, students created a Miss Frizzle-style story about human body systems based on their virtual reality journey through a human body?

My friend and colleague Tracey Pinkin uses augmented and virtual reality for her high school anatomy course, and when I asked her about it, here were her reflections:

"The use of AR and VR in the classroom was the next step in bringing anatomy to life. The challenges of teaching anatomy and physiology in a high school classroom are rooted in budgetary constraints. While textbook illustrations, models, and photocopied diagrams meet basic needs, they cannot replicate an authentic, hands-on experience. With the shift in education toward more problem-based learning and an emphasis on soft skills, such as collaboration, AR and VR provide the opportunity for students to practice these skills daily. Also, students with an inability to focus or those who struggle with learning differences can benefit from a more interactive educational experience that textbooks cannot provide."

A great variety of virtual and augmented reality applications exist that are excellent for use in the classroom. One of these is HP Reveal (formerly named Aurasma), with which you can layer hidden text messages, videos, and photos in everyday items and illustrations. Picture this (pun partially intended): a traditional poster presentation all about a famous scientist with pictures of Einstein and short factoids about his life, accomplishments, and how they have affected our current scientific knowledge. Using the HP Reveal app, you can scan over the poster to a picture of Einstein in the laboratory and a video pops up of a student demonstrating a lab that Einstein used in his own laboratory or telling you bonus

Scan QR code to view the project.

facts! Here is an example of one of my classes' work from our very first HP Reveal project.

As educators, we know the power of visuals and visualization. The question is how can we harness that power to become superheroes of teaching in the classroom? How can we use that power to build critical thinking and observational skills of our students? How can we transition our students from content consumers to content creators through photography, videography, and virtual reality? What's your move?

Resources to Help Create or Use Visuals in Your Classroom:

- **Your Smartphone:** Yes, seriously, the best camera you have is the one you've got, which for many, myself included, is our good old smartphone! Just simply using your phone and the photographs you take is powerful. Even selfies with something you want to show your students, be it a location, a bird, a sign ... anything. If I am not visible in a photo or video I share, my scientists often ask, "Where are you?" They connect to content I collect, create, and share. Something about knowing I was there and took the photo or shot the video allows my scientists to connect better. If you need help with smartphone photography or videography, let me know, I can help!

- **Google Arts and Culture App:** Premade expeditions that are (or were!) found in the Google Expeditions app will be absorbed into Google Arts and Culture in June 2021. There, you will find augmented and virtual reality simulations already made and free for use in addition to some great opportunities for arts and humanities integrations. One of my favorites (in addition to VR/AR) is the art selfie option. Check this app out, ASAP.

- **CoSpaces Edu:** Great online platform that allows you and your learners to be AR and VR content creators, and it even has an optional coding component! It is complete with great teacher resources and tutorials for both educators and learners. I love using it in tandem with Merge Cube.

- **Merge Cube:** This tool is literally a foam cube you can set in front of you, hold, rotate, or even collaborate with a partner to experience augmented reality. This powerful tool has its own app; there are several, in fact, filled with preloaded augmented reality games and instructional options. Combine this with CoSpaces Edu, and your learners can become creators of augmented reality content. You will need a device, such as a smartphone or iPad, to use in tandem with the Merge Cube.

- *Reality Bytes: Innovative Learning Using Augmented and Virtual Reality* by Christine Lion-Bailey, Jesse Lubinsky, and Dr. Micah Shippee: This book is a powerhouse of information and ideas for implementing augmented and virtual reality. Check it out!

- **HP Reveal app:** Embedding video or photos into everyday images, audiences can use this app to scan an object to reveal what is embedded. This is what my learners used to create an interactive display of scientist Raquel Fleskes (grade three) and a global climate change mural (grade four).

- **Virtuali-Tee:** This is literally a T-shirt that has embedded augmented reality illustrating human body systems along with narrations you can access with the free app on a smartphone, tablet, or iPad.

- **Piktochart:** An online tool to create diagrams, visual aids, and graphics. I use this often to create visual notes or concept mapping with visuals rather than traditional box and line methods, although you can do that as well.

EDUCATOR ASIDE

Julie Theim (Instagram: @jorgenja)

adaptive art specialist and National Geographic Certified Educator

"The summer air of the Arctic was crisp with the slightest ..." I begin but am immediately cut off with a squeak from a student beside me.

"OMG, Mrs. Theim. I am standing next to you on the ship!"

I continue, "Yes, you sure are! ... the slightest fog rolling ..."

"Mrs. Theim! Look up! What kind of birds are those?"

I check the sky in the photo on my teacher iPad. "Those are the guillemots. They nest along that cliff you see in front of you and can gather in groups of thousands. That's why you see so many of them. The best advice I was given by one of the naturalists was that you just need to remember that when you look up to close your mouth, as you wouldn't want any bird poop landing in there!"

As I look up from my iPad-guided VR tour, I see several students quickly move their heads to look up through their VR goggles and instantly shut their mouth, and I giggle to myself and breathe this moment in as a top-notch classroom exploration experience. Nailed it!

Storytelling about my expedition to Svalbard was really an immersive phototelling (as I have come to call it) experience. Through use of VR technology, along with my Garmin Virb (360 camera), I am able to bring my students with me on the expedition. I can hold conversations with them, as well as teach them through the scenes. Using Google Tour Creator, I built a virtual field trip of my experience as a Grosvenor Teacher Fellow with National Geographic and Lindblad Expeditions in the High Arctic of Svalbard. Svalbard is the closest archipelago to the North Pole. In June 2018, I was aboard the *National Geographic Explorer* and we circumnavigated Svalbard. The expedition was nothing short of exhilarating and amazing beyond words, and throughout it, I was thinking about *how* I would be able to share the experience with my students in a way that effectively sparks their curiosity.

Using the strategy share of building a virtual field trip was the knowledge base for my K–6 students in beginning their art projects for our annual art show. Every year we display and hold a school-wide gallery of projects. They usually connect to a theme we have studied and can, in turn, visually share with our viewers. The year of the Arctic theme, walruses as big as kindergarteners, a wall-sized map with silk hoop Arctic animals, and a variety of polar bear projects lined our halls— more than five hundred pieces of art that all stemmed from the VR field trip experience. My artists were now travelling art explorers; they, too, were on an expedition. Because of that integration of technology in the classroom, the learning outcome was strong, the excitement lasted well beyond their art projects, and even now, two years later, my students will bring up their expedition to the Arctic. I get questions like, "When can we go back to the Arctic? Where is your next expedition, Mrs. Theim? Can I stand next to you on the ship again? Where else can you take us?" You see, when education can go beyond the walls of the classroom, that is when the magic happens within the classroom!

CHAPTER TWELVE

STORYTELLING

Have I ever told you about the time I was nearly eaten by a jaguar? It's August 2018, and I'm in the Peruvian Amazon as a member of an expedition team studying thermal river systems. It is my first year on the team and the third day in the field. Although it is "winter" or dry season in the Southern Hemisphere, the jungle is hot and humid. On top of it all, I am working alongside a boiling river. Yes, you read that right, a river so hot that it boils. I am wearing a long-sleeve, moisture-wicking shirt and long, convertible pants meant for working in the field. Sweat drips from every pore of my body, but the long sleeves and pants are preventing me from getting bitten by unknown insects and mosquitoes possibly carrying malaria. There have been no documented cases of malaria in this area of the Amazon, but I like to take this precaution. No one enjoys having itchy mosquito bites anyway.

My task today is to collect 360-degree imagery along the river. The goal is to have only the natural surroundings visible, which means I get the added adventure of playing hide and seek with a camera that can see 360 degrees. This type of work places me in multiple precarious locations and positions. I have to hide under rock outcroppings with tarantulas and, on one occasion, bats; climb high into trees with thorned bark, branches, and leaves; and my personal favorite, assume a *Mission Impossible*-like position where I lay flat on my back, hanging over and off a rocky ledge, arching my back down toward a ten-foot drop. Rather than allow fear to infiltrate my head during these times, I instead think about how bad@$$ I will look in a movie or on the cover of *National Geographic* as an explorer. Thanks to my field partner, Wesley Della Volla, there are actually fantastic shots of me completing this work.

Picture of me setting up my 360 camera in the Peruvian Amazon, taken by Wesley Della Volla.

Me on the banks of Shanay-Timpishka, the Boiling River of the Amazon.

photo credit: Wesley Della Volla

Today is day three of this task. We are taking our time to document this section of jungle to track change and conservation efforts over time. We want to make sure the shots are perfect and that we can connect them, one picture to another, to make a seamless path along the river for documentation. Over the last two days, some shots were not good enough and we had to retake them. Today was "clean up" day; we were retaking photos that needed better lighting and there were still a few shots of iconic locations that we had not yet been able to get. Today was a big day. We needed to finish, and we needed perfection.

We did *not* need a jaguar encounter, but that's exactly what we were about to get.

Shooting with a 360 camera can be challenging all on its own, but add in the necessity of shooting using Bluetooth and in difficult lighting conditions, and things can be very frustrating. I had been having major issues shooting with the Bluetooth option which I needed to use in order to be hidden from view in these particular photos. It was taking a long time to register the command from my phone to the camera, and being in these compromising positions was not always comfortable, as you can imagine.

I set up my camera, prepared the Bluetooth connection, took a test shot of me in the frame then began to find my hiding location. To do this, I use my phone's screen to see what the camera can see as I walk away to hide. The Bluetooth has, thus far, required me to be within 1.5 meters or about five feet of the camera itself, another piece of the frustrating puzzle. For the shot I want at this particular moment, I have two options. One is behind the buttress roots of a massive tree; for the other, I had to climb into some foliage on the side of a rock outcrop.

I tried the tree idea first. That option would be easier, just to crouch behind the large buttress roots. I set up the camera on its tripod, connected the Bluetooth, and hid behind the massive roots. I tried for what seemed like an eternity to snap the shot to no avail. The Bluetooth connection was not strong enough from that location. Maybe it was the thickness of those buttress roots. All I know for sure is that it was hot, and I was ready to wrap this up. My patience was wearing thin. Option two was to climb into foliage along a rock outcrop, which ended up being much more difficult and tested my patience even further. What's more, the foliage was filled with thorns that clung to my clothing and hair as if its very existence depended on that grasp. When I settled within the leaves, I realized quickly that those thorns had a tight grasp on me. I literally could not move my head from side to side or change body positions at all. Wesley was resting comfortably under a rock outcrop and never had I felt more jealous during this ordeal. The Bluetooth connection was spotty and testing my patience once more. *Are you kidding me right now?* I thought as I was pinned in the foliage unable to get out. The good news was the Bluetooth connection was still "live"; it was just stuck in processing, meaning the image I was attempting to capture had not been taken just yet. I try to free myself from the thorns and I realized that not only was I stuck, but I would also, embarrassingly, need to ask Wesley to help free me.

That's when I heard it.

The growl.

There was a jaguar close enough to me that I could hear it.

Seriously?

Unsure if I was really hearing the sound, I called to Wesley, who at the same time made eye contact with me and I could tell by his expression, he did in fact also hear the jaguar.

Jaguars are ambush predators. You will most likely never see it; *it sees you.* They are vicious in their attack, going straight for the cranium, meaning instant (hopefully) death. My mind was racing with so many thoughts.

Can I get this picture before I die? It's so close. I am going to get this picture, and it's totally fine. The jaguar will just kill me, but my team will later find my camera with the epic shot, and at my funeral, there will be stories of how I died doing what I loved. And that's OK, too. This jaguar is going to go straight for my head; I will feel nothing. The sight afterward will horrify my teammates, but that picture will be taken. Everything will turn out OK.

As these thoughts are blowing through my consciousness, along with thousands of others, I can feel the jaguar breathing on the side of my head as I hear its growling sound. My hair is literally moving from the force of the jaguar's breathing . . .

This is it, I thought.

I hear the picture on the 360 camera snap, and I Incredible Hulk myself out of the thorns. Moments before, I could not move a centimeter within the grasp of those thorns, but at this moment, adrenaline kicked in and I was free . . . from the plants at least. Wesley sees me break and we both run as if our lives depend on it. (Because they do!)

We run and jump from rock to rock amid the boiling water, steam kissing our legs and feet as we try to outrun a jaguar.

Hearts pounding, bodies sweating even more than they were just from the heat.

Out of breath, we make it to our base camp somehow, and there is no time for questions.

We are alive, somehow.

As we meet up with our expedition team at camp, Wesley and I recall the details of our day, incredibly proud and lucky to be alive *and* with the photography project wrapped up. We tell our tale, and the team is impressed and also glad to see us still alive at this moment.

Incredible. Unbelievable, in fact.

Andrés, our principal investigator, asks for a few more details about the jaguar and its sounds. We replayed and even imitated (poorly) the sounds and observations during which Andrés begins to smile at us.

"So, that was actually a hummingbird," he responds with a smile decorating his face like a birthday cake, and we all join in boisterous laughter.

I share this story often when students or even adults ask if I ever saw or experienced something scary in the field. I also use it to talk about perspective and context clues with students. I even use it as an invitation for them to share stories from their lives.

When have you experienced something scary that turned out to be not such a big deal?

If you heard these types of sounds but were alone in your house, what might it have been?

What if you were in a grocery store and heard these sounds?

Can you retell this story from the perspective of the hummingbird? What about from the perspective of Andrés?

Storytelling is an incredibly powerful teaching tool, whether it's being used as a hook, a common experience, a way to enhance or make a connection to classroom content, forming or fostering relationships and connections to our students, or anything in between. Stories are powerful.

They do not have to be from personal experience or as elaborate as mine; they can be a news article, storybook, folktale, joke, picture book, riddle, primary source—anything. What makes it powerful is that it creates a connection; humans strive for connection to other people, objects, events, groups, and experiences, making storytelling a super-glue of sorts that connects ideas, thoughts, concepts, and even people.

When was the last time you heard a good story?

When was the last time you shared a good story?

How can we use it to connect our learners to information or content?

How can we use it to form or foster relationships between our-selves as educators and our learners?

The reason the Boiling River Project exists and our field team com-pletes the work we do in the Peruvian Amazon is based on a story, a legend that has been passed down for years from the time of the Inka recalling the arrival and greed of Spanish conquistadors. The story told of a river that was so hot it boiled and cannibalistic tribes that inhabited the surrounding area. Based on that story, geoscientist Andrés Ruzo decided to investigate and found details of the story to be true. This has forever changed my perspective; it has changed my attention to detail in listening to stories, particularly myths and legends specific to different cultural groups. It has also infiltrated my integration of myths and legends to my own content, allowing them to drive investigation and scientific questioning. Legends, myths, and folklore are founded in the human need to explain the unexplainable. That, at its foundation, is science, right? We experience, see, or know of something that "does not make sense" or catches our attention, and we look to explain it, figure out its "story" so to speak, and share that with others. Yes, that is science at its core.

One year with my fifth-grade scientists, I ran a project called "Myth Busters" where we investigated myths from African culture that sought to explain a scientific phenomenon, like the West African tale *Why Mosquitoes Buzz in People's Ears*. We read together, then got down to the "science" of it all. Sometimes the stories would be what we consider in modern science to be accurate, while others, like this particular tale, are not scientifically sound in the traditional and modern sense.

Nonetheless, they hinge upon observation, analysis, and drawing conclusions based on those observations in order to create these stories and explanations of phenomena to the best of their ability. In retrospect, I realize how culturally insensitive the title of the project "Myth Busters" is and will no longer use it. I will also be more sensitive to the fact that some cultures use stories, myths, and legends like this still today as integral to their very identity and belief system. Indigenous knowledge, customs, and beliefs are critical in the Western world of science and must coexist in this space. I continually work to be more sensitive and attuned to this truth. The point is that stories and storytelling are integral to science content and understanding. What a beautiful opportunity to integrate the arts and cultures from around the world into scientific investigation, honoring their Indigenous knowledge in tandem with modern scientific investigation. The act of learning these stories and, furthermore, sharing them is an honor in itself. If you are fortunate enough to receive stories from an Indigenous community member, understand that this is truly sacred; it is an honor not bestowed on humans outside of the Indigenous community often. This gift of stories and knowledge should be used and shared not only with permission from the community in which you received the gift but with the utmost respect and honor.

Rethinking Professional Development

In 2017, I submitted an application to the Donna Sterling Exemplary Science Teaching Award committee in the hopes of receiving funds for a professional development opportunity. I had no doubt that my application would be rejected. You see, I wasn't asking to go to a conference, take a class, or do any of the other usual professional development activities available to elementary school teachers. No, I was proposing to join a field science expedition team to the Peruvian Amazon to work alongside scientists to experience field and expedition science myself in order to improve my ability to plan such experiences for my students. Crazy, right?

Two months later, however, I opened an email, which I must have then read at least fifty times. I'd won! My crazy idea was being funded. Then, in August 2018, my field expedition came to life, and it proved to be everything (plus some!) I had hoped it would be for me personally and professionally. The experience in the field gathering and analyzing data, the lessons I learned about field team dynamics, and the ideas I dreamed up for my classroom were all incredible. Honestly, I am still processing, prioritizing, and creating classroom curriculum based on all that I experienced. Additionally, Andrés Ruzo, the principal investigator for the team, even asked me to join the Boiling River Project as a permanent team member and educational team leader.

While my experience seems like a dream, what I've come to realize is that having opportunities like this isn't too much to ask. In fact, we owe this type of opportunity to all educators. We have to rethink professional development—what it is, what it looks like, and how it must actually help educators improve their craft and content knowledge. I contend that it needs to be authentic and immersive. We need to see what skills in our content area specifically look like in the real world in order to provide these experiences for our learners. Not just a workshop, a conference session, a college course, or a similar status quo opportunity that we say is "real." We need field experiences that *are* real.

I want you to take a moment and visualize what such an opportunity would look like for you. What would you do? What would you learn? How would such an experience change the way you teach? Now, take some time to think about how you can make this happen. I know it won't be easy, but I promise it's worth fighting for.

Interested in professional development opportunities that get you into the field rather than sitting in a classroom? Here are a few ideas to get you started.

- **Grosvenor Teacher Fellowship:** A partnership between Lindblad Expeditions and the National Geographic Society that selects educators to go on expeditions around the world.
- **GeoCamp Iceland:** An educational project dedicated to increasing knowledge and understanding in natural sciences with practical and active learning.
- **Teacher at Sea:** Provides teachers with hands-on, real-world research experience working at sea with world-renowned NOAA scientists aboard NOAA research ships.
- **Homeward Bound:** A transformational leadership initiative for women with a background in STEMM (science, technology, engineering, mathematics, medicine) from around the world.
- **Project Archaeology:** Open to social studies and science teachers to learn about Project Archaeology's inquiry-based learning curriculum, how to use it, and empower them to share it with other educators.
- **Fulbright Teacher Fellowships:** Offer a variety of professional development opportunities including teacher exchange programs.
- **PolarTREC:** Secondary educators (grades six through twelve) participate in field research in the Artic or Antarctic regions for three to six weeks.
- **Fund for Teacher Fellowships:** Educators propose a learning opportunity and project of their own to develop skills, knowledge, and confidence that will directly impact students and student achievement.

My first ever expedition was funded by a grant through the Virginia Association of Science Teachers, my state organization for science educators. State organizations are great places to look for localized funding. I have been able to complete many different projects out of grant opportunities in this way, from purchasing geology field equipment to binoculars and watercolor materials for nature journaling with my students.

I also learn a lot through social media, especially Twitter chats like #scitlap and #EducatorExplorer.

Professional development, the kind you really need, is going to be up to you to find and utilize. My friend Tracey Taylor offers this reflection from her own experiences:

"Several years back, the teacher next door to my classroom would periodically ask me what books I was reading. It wasn't until after a few years of this question that she revealed that in her eyes I had become much like Tom Cruise's character in the vintage movie *Cocktail* to her, always had a book or two or three that I was reading, usually for research or for new ideas to implement and develop my practice and craft of teaching. It turned out to be something she appreciated about me. At the time, I was bound and determined to not have boring classes where the students, in the absence of authentic learning experiences, would find a myriad of inappropriate ways in which to entertain themselves. I refused to be the teacher that never let kids touch stuff. I was refusing to be the teacher who created a classroom or course that students didn't want to come into because it was a waste of their time. I would love for you to know that now, compared to those days, there is *so* much more out there because of this influx of teachers producing, sharing, collaborating, and writing books that if you want it, it is easy to go out and get it, whatever that 'it' is for you in this moment, be it student engagement, creating engaging content experiences, using technology to enhance your instructional strategies or anything else. Let me encourage your first small steps to get what you want and what your students need. Get connected with other educators on social media, download a book, listen to a podcast, seek out your own professional development sources, spend some time going after 'it.'"

EDUCATOR ASIDE

Peter Cameron (@petectweets)
teacher and adventurer, mrcshareseaseblog.wordpress.com

I like a good story, and I also like to tell one. Since I reside on the shores of Lake Superior in Thunder Bay, Ontario, it should come as no surprise that many of my stories involve water in one form or another. I love to share childhood stories of fishing and exploring with my father along the many creeks that feed Lake Superior or more recent adventures with my own wife and son gliding atop the snow for seemingly endless kilometers through the northern wilderness. In sharing my stories with my students, I inspire in them a quest to explore their own passions and begin to create, weave, and write their own personal life stories. Through the creating and sharing of life stories, we can't help but learn. Experience is life's greatest teacher.

You never know the effect and reach a story can have.

As a young student, I fondly remember watching the National Film Board's *Paddle to the Sea*. It's a story about a young Indigenous boy who carves a wooden replica of himself paddling a canoe. The story follows the journey of the little canoe through the Great Lakes to its eventual destination, the Atlantic Ocean. The story connected me to the Great Lakes and opened my eyes to a world beyond Thunder Bay and Lake Superior. I now bring *Paddle to the Sea* to my own class and harness the power of technology to help my students track Paddle's journey in "real time" via Google Earth.

Although there was never a doubt that my students had a firm understanding of just how great the Great Lakes were, something was still missing. I always struggled to find a way to help my students understand that they were also at risk. It's a hard concept to grasp when you live on the largest freshwater lake in the world. It seems so vast, so endless, so untouched.

Two stories, one that I wrote and one that I learned, allowed me to bring my students the knowledge and understanding I believed they were missing. My work with Google Earth and National Geographic Education brought me to Google headquarters and eventually led me to team with an incredible group of educators to pitch an idea for a Teacher Authored Voyageur (TAV) story, which we called "Blue Gold." The idea was to have students use Google Earth to take a modern-day journey down the Great Lakes. This would help them understand just how great the Great Lakes are, as well as realize that the lakes are at risk. The story ends with a call to action. Our idea was voted the story "Most Likely to Change the World," and we learned it would become the first TAV to be launched on Google Earth. I couldn't wait to put the Voyageur story in the hands of my students and watch them navigate "Blue Gold." What they would find within it would be sure to amaze, challenge, and inspire them!

While all this was happening, I also learned the story of Nokomis Josephine Mandamin. On a cool, overcast day in late April, my son Kai and I decided to take our French exchange student Renaud on a short bike ride around a small lake that connects to Lake Superior. As we were riding, we passed a woman dressed in traditional Anishinaabe clothing, carrying a staff in one hand and a copper bucket in the other. After we passed, my son inquired about who she may be and what she might be doing. As we rode, I suggested that we could turn around and he could ask her the very questions that were on my mind as well. However, the moment passed and the opportunity was lost.

And then, it happened! On a Saturday afternoon in mid-May, I opened a magazine and found a book review about a story titled "The Water Walker." Could the main character possibly be the mysterious woman Kai, Renaud, and I had seen on that day in April? I had to find out. Within twenty-four hours, I had found "The Water Walker."

Nokomis Josephine Mandamin's story is simply incredible and inspiring. One day a wise *ogimaa* told her: "In your lifetime, the day will come when an ounce of water costs more than an ounce of gold. What are you going to do about it?" Josephine acted. Along with other women, men, and young people, she walked around all five Great Lakes to raise awareness of our need to protect *nibi* (water).

Ironically, Josephine was from Thunder Bay. I simply cannot explain why I hadn't heard her story until then. But I now knew her story, and my son and students would learn it, too. On a beautiful spring day, Josephine came to my classroom. For the first time, I shared "Blue Gold" and the virtual field trip around the Great Lakes with my students, then Josephine shared her story of her actual walk around the Great Lakes. Amazingly, a documentary team from Google Earth was present to capture the story. My students were so inspired that they established the "Junior Water Walkers," an initiative that would see them adopt a body of water, learn about it, then work to protect it. Eventually they would walk at their body of water. My students shared Josephine Mandamin's story and their initiative with other classes and invited them to join the "Junior Water Walkers." To date, over two hundred classes from around the world have joined together to honor Josephine and protect water.

Josephine Mandamin is no longer with us, but her story lives on. What stories will you share with your students? What stories will they create? How will their stories change the world?

CHAPTER THIRTEEN

PLACE-BASED EDUCATION

I run my fingers along the seams of granite stones placed so precisely that not even a sheet of paper can be slipped between them. No mortar between the stones. *What a marvel in engineering and design,* I think to myself as I continue to examine the architecture of the structure. My fingers find a trapezoid-shaped niche, then windows and doorways with this same shape. *This must be some mistake,* I think to myself, *but that's a lot of mistakes in the same structure that has such precision.*

"Those are no mistake," Eduardo, my guide, says to me. He must have read my puzzled expression as I investigated the stones.

"The Inka were master builders, engineers, and architects. That shape withstands earthquakes. The Inka knew the power and strength in that shape. Even the walls of structures have that shape. Look here," he says as he directs my attention to a wall he is standing next to. I follow it

Stones in architecture of the Inka are so closely matched that no mortar is present; it is unnecessary.

and observe how it begins a few inches from his feet but nearly touches his head. *That's geometry,* I think to myself. *They knew the exact angle to create these trapezoid and triangle-shaped spaces, the exact angles to best withstand seismic activity.* I really need the "mind blown" emoji here.

As we continue along the last fifteen kilometers of the Inka Trail to Machu Picchu, Eduardo shows me every building, terrace, fountain, and purification station along the way. He explains the history and the religious significance of structures and features; he even teaches me some Quechua, one of the languages of the Inka still used today. It is fascinating. I am immersed in the culture and history. When we make it to Inti Punku, or Sun Gate, I have an unusual experience. I am no longer Becky; I am transported to the thirteenth century. I am a new Inkan messenger, sent with a message for the inhabitants of Machu Picchu. As I scale the last of the steps to the gate, make it through the archways, and see Machu Picchu, I feel light, accomplished, and ready to sprint to the temples to bring my message. *The Spanish conquistadors are coming,* is my message. In an instant, I transport back to 2018, shoulder to shoulder with Eduardo. It is incredible; I feel connected. I feel called to be there.

That's the power of place. That's what I want my scientists to feel wherever we are studying.

BRINGING SCIENCE HOME

When we travel, we immerse ourselves in the place we visit. We learn about the culture, food, music, and history, and we ask endless questions. At the end of our expedition to this new location, near or far, tears often fill our eyes, sinking feelings fill our abdomen, and we long for just a few more days, a few more experiences. That's powerful.

Why aren't we taking this approach in learning or teaching?

Why aren't we making an effort to immerse ourselves and our young scientists in our own spaces? After all, it's where we are each day. Why aren't we immersed in that history, culture, and change over time?

Can you imagine the type of deep-seated learning that would occur if we took this travel and immersion approach to our own learning spaces and communities?

I am embarrassed to admit to you (too late now) that I know more about Indigenous tribes of the Amazon and the Inka than I do about the Indigenous tribes of the Chesapeake, the very location I have lived my entire life. Through my own reflection about why and how this could happen, I realize that since the arrival of Europeans to North America, the entitlement of these Europeans allowed for the erasure of Indigenous cultures, belief systems, families . . . everything. Whole communities were threatened, cleared out, enslaved, and banished from the locations their ancestors inhabited for thousands of years. The European colonization of North America left very few to no voices in decision-making, much less school curriculum development. By stealing land and treating whole populations as less than human to the point of extinction for some cultures, of course I never learned about them in my traditional schooling; that piece of history is completely missing. In the last few years and continuing today, Indigenous communities are being empowered to speak, be heard, be seen, and their history, the true history of whole continents, is being uncovered, learned, and slowly integrated into curricula, but we have a long, long way to go.

If you are interested in diving deeper into Indigenous studies and a more complete telling of the history of the United States in particular, consider reading *An Indigenous Peoples' History of the United States* by Roxanne Dunbar-Ortiz.

It's time to disrupt this model. Place-based education is not only an engaging way to deliver our content standards, but it's also important to our role in society as human beings and stewards of our spaces. Especially in the area where I live, we are privileged to have a lot of history, from Indigenous tribes to European colonization, the American Revolutionary War, and the American Civil War. We even have the location of the first trial by ducking of a witch in Virginia! What better way to understand our own history than to immerse ourselves in it on-site?

Every location is different and unique. Every place, near or far, has different lenses through which to explore geography and landscape—physical, cultural, ecological. It is time to take advantage of that! You can start wherever you'd like or wherever your content feels most natural.

In North America in particular, one common thread of history is that of Indigenous peoples, the original protectors of the land. That's a great place to start from a cultural perspective or even a historical context. My fourth-grade scientists have a year-long watershed rehabilitation study and project that ties beautifully with social studies content in discovering the physical and geographic regions of the state of Virginia. They also dive into European settlement (as described by the Virginia standards), specifically studying the Revolutionary War, Civil War, and land in present-day Virginia. This is the perfect natural area to incorporate place-based studies that travel through the cultural landscape from the beginning of Indigenous presence. While our state standards do not specifically mandate that we teach this important history, I believe that we need to address Indigenous people and their origins here in North America and in the state of Virginia specifically. The fact that European intruders are referred to as "settlers" in the first place negates the fact that they stole the land, traditions, and livelihood of Indigenous people who inhabited the land for thousands of years prior to European intrusion. The oppression and decimation of the Indigenous people of Virginia cannot continue to be neglected; in fact, we must seek opportunities to learn more. If we get to know the Indigenous land protectors and their knowledge, customs, lifestyle, and beliefs, we can get further in touch with our environment. This is a privilege, an honor, and a responsibility entrusted to those fortunate enough to be provided insight and knowledge into Indigenous teachings, customs, and culture. This honor should not be taken lightly, and passing on this knowledge to whomever you've entrusted should be done in a respectful manner. This honor in learning and passing on knowledge also allows us to dive deeper into the implications of European appearance here beginning in 1492, or earlier in some North American areas. The names of localities may take on larger significance, and we can make sense of living history and perhaps even peek into the future based on our own patterns of behaviors. While, again, none of this is mandated by Virginia standards of learning, or perhaps your own national, state, or local standards, it is imperative to spreading the true history of any area, especially in North America.

To begin our work, I project this land claim map created by native-land. ca on the board to show my scientists Indigenous land claims in our local area of Virginia. They also receive a laminated copy at their workstations. Immediately they begin calling out observations.

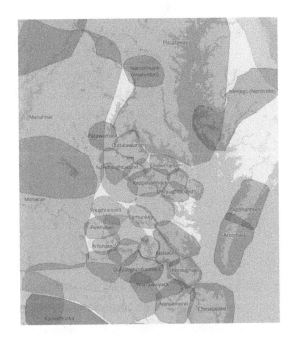

"Chesapeake! No way! I live there!" one scientist announces.

"I've heard of Nansemond-Suffolk school," another adds.

"Kiptopeke is where I go for summer camp. Why isn't it on there?" asks a third scientist.

"I see Powhatan!" a fourth scientist adds.

"Those are weird names."

"Where is Virginia Beach? I thought you said this was a map of our area?"

"What do you think this is?" I ask the group.

I am introducing them to the geographic regions of Virginia, but first come Indigenous cultures and customs, followed by influences of European intrusion upon Indigenous communities over time, as well as significant historic events in our region, the Tidewater or Coastal Plain. Is that a part of standards I am expected to cover? Nope. I make the cognizant and informed decision to incorporate this into my content, in addition to the standards, because it shows a more complete picture; it helps my scientists think deeper about the implications of historic events, and it allows for immersion into the culture and history of our place. We do this naturally when visiting other locations; we thirst for this knowledge and experience. It allows us to connect and understand, and I believe we need this in our own spaces as well. When we understand the complete history, the details not explicitly stated in mandated standards, true comprehension occurs rather than the memorization of what an arbitrary group thinks is important for learners to know in any given year of development. This also allows us, in particular regard to Indigenous culture, land claims, and stewardship, to honor, understand, and appreciate how the places we live were taken care of long before our existence in them. We owe a lot to Indigenous caretakers, the original inhabitants of our spaces and places.

It is particularly fascinating to get to know the scientific knowledge and understanding of Indigenous groups, which is often much more advanced than what is considered to be modern study and understanding. Think about this a moment. The Inka were so sophisticated in their engineering and design that they needed no mortar between stones. They perfectly created gates around the empire that line up for solstice celebrations. What technology or laboratory facilities did they have?

That is knowledge. *That* is understanding. *That* is observation. *That* is science.

How can we *not* value the knowledge of Indigenous people who discovered things long before "modern study" would? Our society as a whole has missed out by refusing to collaborate, refusing to believe "savages" had anything to offer in terms of intelligence and wisdom, choosing to steal their land rather than seek ways to effectively cohabitate or create a mutualistic relationship between Indigenous folks and themselves. Think about the social-emotional learning and character-building lessons we can glean from this on top of the content knowledge. This is missing from most curricula, but this is our history. We cannot allow time and outdated curricula to dictate the continued erasure of Indigenous culture and the history of North America, in particular. Getting to know Indigenous culture, people, and practices is an honor, a blessing, and not something that *just happens.*

In my experience thus far on my journey to know, understand, and foster connections to Indigenous culture, I have learned that everything, from stories to weaving textiles, fishing techniques, and prayer and ritual, is sacred. It is not meant to be observed clinically or scientifically; it is not meant for the entertainment or use of outsiders. These practices are integral parts of Indigenous life, teaching, and culture. In my own experience, many elders and Indigenous peoples will not openly share their knowledge, stories, customs, and teachings, as they are not meant to be a show or a lesson or shared outside of their sacred intention. This may feel defeating as an outsider seeking knowledge and ways to integrate these components into your teaching, but that is not and was never meant for you. What you *can* do is research and look for more complete anthologies that *do* acknowledge and honor the Indigenous communities in your area. You can also seek guidance from local Indigenous communities, but think through what you are asking, seeking, and expecting from your collaborator. Are you seeking a "show" for your students or deep-seated knowledge and experiences to understand the realities, especially in North America, of what the appearance of European human beings truly did to these communities?

How can we better harness the power of our space and place into our content? How will this enhance learning and personal connection?

EDUCATOR ASIDE

Jen Chavez-Miller (@JenChavezMiller)
faculty, teacher education, Central New Mexico Community College, thinkglobalteachlocal.com

The geographies of schools and classrooms are as diverse as the far reaches of Earth. The concept of *place* has complex, multidimensional, and unique textures. While we educators are intentional in cultivating communities of learners that are accessible, joyful, and rich in opportunities and experiences that connect students to content and each other, we often start within the borders of our classrooms where, indeed, a thriving ecosystem can bloom and sustain.

However, it is when we strive to make the borders of our classrooms permeable that we are able to accomplish the critical and creative work of connecting students to context and the interconnected, symbiotic dynamics of life within our communities and across the planet.

Over two decades as a classroom teacher, I have learned and taught in ways that aim to deconstruct the narrative that school is a place where we prepare students to engage in the world when they are grown and graduates, and instead construct a narrative that students are essential, vibrant, invaluable, and worthy of engaging with the world *now*.

This narrative was co-constructed with students along the banks of the Rio Grande River, an ever-present geographic and historical anchor in our city and state, and for several years, the Bosque—or forest—that borders the Rio Grande was an extension of our classroom. Except for the coldest winter months, our classes would spend Friday mornings in the Bosque. Toting backpacks, water bottles, snacks and sack lunches, colored pencils, journals, and chapter books, we explored and observed the wonders of this enchanting ecosystem in the midst of our city. My middle-school students pursued inquiry of wildlife and safety corridors, bats and the benefits of bat houses among the cottonwood trees, and the impact of non-native species of plants and trees.

Inquiry and place-based learning are natural partners. While I structured each year-long experience in the Bosque to include one or more cycles of inquiry, I allowed time for students to get to know this place. For some, this was familiar stomping grounds. For others, like it was for me as a child growing up here, they had crossed bridges over the Rio Grande but had never been along the banks or wandered under the cottonwood canopy.

My goal is to inspire curiosity and joy, along with a sense of belonging, awe, and love for our place. I keep this idea at the forefront of my thinking and instructional design:

When we know a place, we come to care about that place.

When we care about a place, we work to protect it.

So, we learned to love this place through play, through time to explore. We would build tree-branch forts and little twig boats with leaves for sails that we'd set adrift in the river. We would take a daily rest and lay in a sunny field of grasses and wild sunflowers. Students would find a tree to settle in, and we'd spend quiet moments reading our own books. Our journals filled with nature sketches, creative stories, and accounts of our experiences. We'd migrate through the Bosque along the trails, observing insects, blue-tailed lizards, hummingbirds, hawks, and egrets. We offered abundant kudos to the first person to spot a porcupine in the branches of the tall trees. And I'll never forget the day when a snake zipped past us, across the trail and straight up into a tree!

I was mindful to make curricular connections to our time in the Bosque. Our study of migration began with conversations on the banks of the Rio Grande as we watched flock after flock of Canada geese and sandhill cranes on their seasonal migratory travels. I would read the mythologies of the Ganges River while we sat beside our own river, weaving the ancient yet ever-present narratives of land, water, wildlife, and people. Poetry is particularly beautiful in the cathedral of cottonwoods, breathing in the words and imagery while birds added their own unique verse.

When we know a place, we come to care about that place.

When we care about a place, we work to protect it.

Exploration always leads to questions. Why do people leave their trash here? Where do the coyotes go in the day when we're here? What will happen if the Bosque caught fire? Why is the river running so low? Why do bats live here? These questions lead to inquiry projects. How do we convince people not to leave trash in the Bosque? What role do pollinators, including bats, have in the Bosque ecosystem? How do water laws in our state influence the flow and appropriation of water upstream and downstream from where we are?

As a humanities teacher, I recognized that the world was ours to explore through reading, writing, speaking, and listening. I realized that when we combined our study of science and phenomenon through the natural world *and* the study of our human story, we were holistically engaged in *geography*.

I look to the tenets of place-based education to structure opportunities in which students engage in multidisciplinary, experiential inquiry that is born in and for a particular place. I facilitate those connections among students and their connections to place and the broader context of community. This foundational pedagogy then provides the basis for conversations and actions related to social justice (Who has access to outdoor spaces?), advocacy, and taking action, like when my students worked with New Mexico Wild Friends to testify as expert witnesses in committees and on the floor of the state legislature in support of the successful passage of a bill to build wildlife corridors in key areas across the state.

We change the culture of our classrooms when we bring the world in through inquiry, story, and technology. We challenge, inspire, and support our students to become critical thinkers and consumers, develop global competence, and engage in problem-solving. This can—and should—be done in our classrooms to connect students to the world beyond.

However, we change the world when we create opportunities and experiences for students to learn, explore, and take action beyond our classrooms. Our youth deserve to be part of the conversations, part of the process of generating solutions that are informed by their unique, invaluable perspective. Over dozens of Fridays in the Bosque with students, I learned a lesson that continues to transform my teaching: our youth have something to say. They have so much to contribute. And they shouldn't have to wait until they're grown and deemed ready to engage. No, we need them now. That is our work.

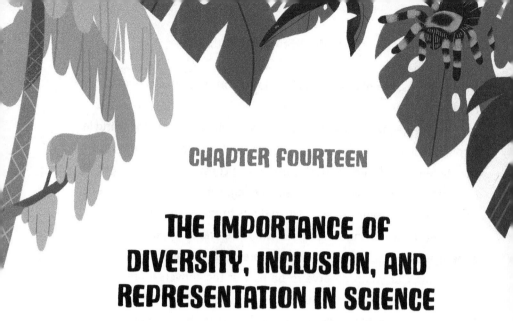

CHAPTER FOURTEEN

THE IMPORTANCE OF DIVERSITY, INCLUSION, AND REPRESENTATION IN SCIENCE

"Wait! If she made the discovery, why do we only ever hear about Crick, Watson, and Wilkins?" one scientist exclaims, referring to Rosalind Franklin's role in understanding the double helix form of DNA.

"So, there is a lot going on with all of this. Dr. Franklin's work led to the eventual discovery of the double helix configuration. Also, as a woman in science, Dr. Franklin was not always heard or taken seriously by other scientists. Most scientists, especially those given recognition and respect, were white males. This is a problem that has been around for a long time. It began before her time, when women were not even allowed an education. Believe it or not, even today, there are women who are not given the respect they deserve in science. It is an even bigger problem for women of color . . ." I try to explain to my third-grade scientists.

"But that's not fair."

"But you're a woman scientist."

"Your team in the Amazon respects you, right?"

The questions and statements pour in as my scientists digest this little nugget of information.

Expedition Maban poster, the team I worked with in the summer of 2019 in the Peruvian Amazon.

"Yes, my scientists, you are right. It's not fair, I am a woman in science, and my team in the Amazon absolutely respects me. But it's not true for me all of the time, and it's not true for all scientists, especially women and especially scientists who are not white," I respond. "It's a big problem, but guess what? We will not be a part of the problem. Every one of you is a scientist, and we respect every person on our team, always," I continue.

"Is that why we study so many different people we have never heard of?" a brave scientist asks.

"Absolutely. We need to hear all of the stories," I reply. "Let's continue with DNA. I want you to meet a friend of mine, Raquel Fleskes, a genetic anthropologist . . ."

MAKING OUR CLASSROOMS MORE EQUITABLE

There is an ancient Chinese proverb that states: "The best time to plant a tree was twenty years ago. The second best time is now." This can be directly applied to representation within science classrooms. The best time to integrate or even explicitly teach and address diversity, inclusion, and representation within your classroom and curriculum was when you first began teaching; the second best time is now. As educators, we must use our teaching superpowers to show that race is a human-created label rather than a biological categorization; utilize teaching practices that are proven effective with students of color; provide equity in access to resources, knowledge, and opportunities; and promote the study of diverse scientists historically and present day. To be advocates for diversity, inclusion, and representation, we have to use every opportunity we have. I wholeheartedly believe that the way we will make a difference in the world is through education. So, my friends, here we go. Now is the time. Let's look at some ways we can work toward social justice in our classrooms.

Diverse Scientists

Diversity is a broad term that encompasses gender, race, age, sexual orientation, ethnicity, religious affiliation, ability, mobility, and more. When we are teaching about scientists, we must be intentional in the figures we choose to represent the field to our students. Scientists come in all ages, sizes, religious affiliations, nationalities, ethnicities, genders, sexual orientations, abilities, and so on. We need to use these figures as mirrors and windows for our students—mirrors referring to those who reflect the demographics represented in your classroom, while windows are figures that provide insight into demographics that are not represented in your classroom. We need to promote that science is for all; we need to show that, demonstrate it in ourselves, and find representation to showcase aspects that we do not ourselves display.

In being a cisgender, white female within the world of science as an educator and in the field on expedition, I am able to reach a certain demographic of young scientists just by being in the field, sharing my story, and integrating my experiences with that of my own young scientists. Another superpower we all have at our own disposal is social media. By using social media to tell my stories to the world, I am able to reach an even broader audience.

I am a mirror, window, and even doorway for girls and those who identify as female who are interested in the sciences. My responsibility does not end there, though, and if you are a cisgender, white male, considered the most prevalent demographic in science, this does not limit your ability to reach different demographics, nor does it mean you are not responsible for integrating social justice. In fact, it might even mean you have a larger responsibility; you might have to work more diligently to find mirrors and windows for your scientists.

In my current placement as an educator, the demographics of my learners are, to the best of my knowledge, primarily white, middle-to-upper class, able-bodied, cisgender humans. They need windows to diversity of all kinds—race, ethnicity, gender, sexual orientation, different mobilities and abilities, and so on. No one is harmed by the infusion of diversity, inclusion, and representation, but *all are harmed* without it. That is why I actively seek literature and human beings from diverse backgrounds for my students to see, hear, and communicate with. It is important that our young scientists not only hear about or passively study diverse humans in science but also interact with them in real time. If physical interaction is not feasible, especially during events such as a global pandemic, video conferencing is a great option, along with email, video messages, and even snail mail.

Additionally, we need to be cognizant of our focus on historic figures and push to include scientists who are making discoveries presently within the science community. We cannot allow our young scientists to believe we know all there is to know or that scientific discovery has ended; that cannot be further from the truth. There are humans doing work currently that may arguably be more important than figures we obsess over, such as Einstein and Newton. Do not misunderstand me here: these historic scientists are important and their discoveries are critical to what we know and study, but there are many more scientists alive now making incredibly important discoveries about our world that we need to incorporate into our content.

How can you locate and connect in real time with scientists who are actively in laboratories or out in the field? Some resources I use are Explore by the Seat of Your Pants, National Geographic Explorer Classroom, Skype a Scientist, and my own social media. On Twitter especially, I am able to connect with scientists around the world from diverse backgrounds. I follow their work and slip into their DMs. Yes, I do. I introduce myself and my goals in connecting with them and see what resources, time, and projects they may have to share or what possibilities there are for collaboration. I speak with my administration about available funds to compensate them for their time and see where the communication takes us.

To find diverse scientists, some great hashtags and handles to check out are #blackbirdersweek, @JedidahIslerPhD, @hood_naturalist, @ravenscimaven, @IndigenousTweets, @TerriHansen, @500queersci, @millionstem, and @BlackAFinSTEM. Never underestimate the power and impact of simply sending a message via social media. My biggest accomplishments, projects, and expeditions are the direct result of this method of communication. I would not be writing this book right now if I had not social media–stalked scientists, educators, and other authors.

Diverse Science Literature

Including the voices, stories, and experiences of diverse scientists can also be accomplished with literature, whether it's a story for elementary-aged scientists or a novel study for older scientists. Here are some titles to get you started.

Coloring Books:
- *Types of Scientists: A Coloring Book for All Ages* by Dr. Semarhy Quiñones-Soto

Younger Scientists:
- *Cece Loves Science* by Kimberly Derting, Shelli R. Johannes, illustrated by Vashti Harrison
- *Sasha Savvy Learns to Code* by Stacia Deutsch and Reshma Saujani
- *Women Who Dared* by Linda Skeers and Livi Gosling
- *Talkin' about Bessie: The Story of Aviator Elizabeth Coleman* by Nikki Grimes, illustrated by E. B. Lewis
- *When the Shadbush Blooms* by Carla Messinger, Susan Katz, illustrated by David Fadden
- *Doc Like Mommy* by Dr. Crystal Bowe
- *Look What Brown Can Do* by T. Marie Harris, illustrated by Neda Ivanova
- *Shark Lady: The True Story of How Eugenie Clark Became the Ocean's Most Fearless Scientist* by Jess Keating, illustrated by Marta Álvarez Miguéns
- *Women in Science: 50 Fearless Pioneers Who Changed the World* by Rachel Ignotofsky
- *Whoosh! Lonnie Johnson's Super Soaking Stream of Inventions* by Chris Barton, illustrated by Don Tate
- *Wangari Maathai* by Franck Prevot, illustrated by Aurélia Fronty
- *She Sang Promise: The Story of Betty Mae Jumper, Seminole Tribal Leader* by J. G. Annino, illustrated by Lisa Desimini

Middle Years Scientists:
- *The Toothpaste Millionaire* by Jean Merrill
- *May Chinn: The Best Medicine* by Ellen Butts and Joyce R. Schwartz
- *Girls Who Code* by Reshma Saujani
- *The Boy Who Harnessed the Wind* by William Kamkwamba and Bryan Mealer
- *Ada Byron Lovelace and the Thinking Machine* by Laurie Wallmark, illustrated by April Chu
- *Reaching for the Moon: The Autobiography of NASA Mathematician Katherine Johnson* by Katherine Johnson

Older Scientists:
- *Braiding Sweetgrass: Indigenous Wisdom, Scientific Knowledge, and the Teachings of Plants* by Robin Wall Kimmerer
- *The Boiling River: Adventure and Discovery in the Amazon* by Andrés Ruzo
- *Broad Band: The Untold Story of the Women Who Made the Internet* by Claire L. Evans
- *Archaeology from Space: How the Future Shapes Our Past* by Sarah Parcak
- *An Indigenous Peoples' History of the United States* by Roxanne Dunbar-Ortiz

While I take a hands-on exploration approach to my science courses, I rarely have a moment to just sit and read to my scientists. I take advantage of times like those five minutes at the end of class when we cannot start something new, but you know what will happen if there is nothing meaningful occupying the time. I also collaborate with general education teachers to suggest literature they can use while we are studying different topics in the laboratory or field station. The opportunity is there; you just have to find what works for you!

Diversity, inclusion, and representation within your curriculum will take whatever form you choose to incorporate. Sometimes it is just as "simple" as a tweak in the humans you study, the issues within science you choose to teach, or the incorporation of varied texts that better represent the essential truth that science itself does not discriminate; science is for all.

I first met Dr. Angerina Jones in 2019 at the Annual Professional Development Institute hosted by the Virginia Association of Science Teachers where she presented a session during which I learned important strategies that have been proven effective for students of color. You can see these in Chapter 8. That session profoundly impacted me as an educator and human being and as a result created a connection between Dr. Jones and I and strengthened my educational practices. Dr. Angerina Jones currently serves as an instructional specialist for Chesapeake City Public Schools and is the founder of Doctored, LLC, an editing company.

EDUCATOR ASIDE

Dr. Angerina Jones (@doctorangerina, @doctoredllc)
instructional specialist

I can vividly recall the first day of my seventh-grade school year in 1988. My recollection has less to do with experiencing overwhelming back-to-school jitters and more to do with utter astonishment. For the first (and only) time in my K–12 educational career, I walked into a classroom governed by an African American teacher. Adding to my shock was the reality that my new African American science teacher was also a man. My jaw dropped and my eyes enlarged as this *unicorn* addressed me with a warm and cheery good morning greeting!

That year, I learned a great deal about science, but I also came to know so much about science leaders who looked like me. My science teacher, Mr. Jackson, ensured that his science lessons *organically* included stories and photos. He also made certain to mention African American science leaders who contributed to the areas we were learning about. For example, we learned about Percy Lavon Julian during a unit on plants, and when using scales, we learned about J.H. Hunter, who patented a portable weight scale in 1896. When asked why we hadn't learned about these people before, Mr. Jackson replied, "Well, it could be because they [other teachers] didn't know or because they did and didn't see the significance in telling you!" My classmates and I engaged in a conversation about how unfair it was for teachers to perpetuate a one-sided approach to teaching, but we realized that Mr. Jackson, in many ways, was an anomaly. He consistently gave us an opportunity to peer into the rich heritage and vast contributions of African American scientists. Our window seat view into the contributions of African American science leaders was not limited to the twenty-eight days of February and extended beyond the surface learning, which included the honorable mentions of George Washington Carver and Charles Drew. His intentionality to integrate instruction was one of the things that inspired me to become a teacher, and throughout my twenty-two years in education, my conviction regarding social justice makes me ensure instruction remains desegregated.

An alarming fact is that, based on the composition of teachers, most students attending public school in the United States will matriculate through their K–12 educational years without ever having an African American teacher. Putting the public school teacher composition issue into perspective, the National Center for Educational Statistics (NCES) reported that there were 3.8 million K–12 public school teachers in the United States during the 2015–2016 school year and of that, an estimated 256,000, or 6 percent, were African American. Enrollment during that school year totaled 50.33 million students. This means that one in every twenty teachers of those 50.33 million children was African American.

The percentage of African American teachers at the time of NCES's report in 2015 and now, in 2020, is grossly different than it was sixty-five years ago. In the 1950s, teaching was the profession for 50 percent of all African Americans. However, in the last half of the twentieth century and twenty years into the twenty-first century, the number of African American teachers has drastically decreased. Scholars attribute this regression to the 1954 case of *Brown v. Board of Education* of Topeka, Kansas. Throughout the years of 1954–1965, a startling 38,000 African American teachers lost their jobs through desegregation in seventeen states and border states, and just over a decade after *Brown v. Board of Education*, 67 percent of African American teachers were demoted in 1965 alone.

Though the aim of the *Brown v. Board of Education* decision was to integrate public schools, African American teachers and students incurred the unfathomable costs of the ruling: the loss of role models and the influence of cultural elders through termination and demotion, as well as the cessation of culturally relevant teaching. Mr. Jackson, a product of both segregation and desegregation, understood the importance of having all of it, so he worked, unbeknownst to my seventh-grade self, to expose my class to relevant cultural references. I included the aforementioned research, first as a point of awareness, but secondly, as a point for action. Considering the current teacher composition, the likelihood of students having a "Mr. Jackson" as a teacher is very slim; however, that doesn't mean science instruction has to be sans Mr. Jackson's pedagogical strategy to desegregate science instruction.

When considering what needs to happen to desegregate science instruction, an African proverb comes to mind: "Half education is more dangerous than no education." For far too long, BIPOC children have been recipients of partial education, evidenced in the presentation of half-truths presented over the course of 180 instructional days. The adverse effect of science education with fractional truth is a reason many BIPOC children do not pursue careers in STEM and why the achievement gap is widening. Sadly, BIPOC children do not see themselves reflected in

STEM professions, and they suffer with low self-image because they have not seen positive cultural images or the influence of their culture in the world. Learning half of a truth has been, and continues to be, detrimental.

The field of education needs brave teachers who will stand proxy and deliver culturally relevant instruction that provides a mirror and closes gaps. Thus, I propose three ways to organically desegregate science instruction: lessons, literature, and leaders. The first step is to plan lessons that intentionally include a wide range of learning modalities to ensure every type of learner will be able to absorb and process the information. Secondly, desegregation necessitates the inclusion of literature that is a reflection of diversity. The use of culturally relevant literature, posters, and other visual resources act as mirrors and windows. Finally, the incorporation of pertinent science leaders is equally important, as it reduces stereotypes and provides inspiration.

I contend that desegregating science instruction is not an arduous task. It simply takes methodical planning and intentionality (which we already do). Desegregation is essential! As social justice advocates, we owe a wholly truthful education to our students.

CHAPTER FIFTEEN

THE EXPLORER'S MINDSET

"**I** wonder how many turtles there are."

"How do we know if they are male or female?"

"What do they need to survive? How can we make sure they have everything here?"

"I think we need to tell other people about them so they do not mistreat them."

"How can we track them? How do we know if one of them dies or if one of them escapes?"

"Can we plan an investigation?"

The questions, the curiosities roll in.

I have brought my third-grade scientists to a garden on campus that is inhabited by box turtles for some simple observation and nature journaling, which has spiraled into a flurry of questions.

Perfect.

"All right, Explorers, you got it. Let's investigate all of these questions; let's make a plan. With your questions, let's form small teams to tackle them and take some action. Are you ready?" I respond to the mob of explorers ready to pounce on the opportunity to be stewards, scholars, and scientists in this very moment. Before long, small teams of students have plans, demands, and ideas that fill the entire "turtle garden" with energy.

"Here's a list of what we need for the investigation," one scientist says as she hands me a list of equipment she has planned for her team.

"OK, when we do this expedition, we need to either wear clothes we can get dirty to school or pack them. This could get messy," a team member adds.

"We're going to count how many turtles there are!" exclaims a third team member.

"And we're going to track gender and location each day." A new small group runs to me with crumpled paper plans to show off.

"We want to stop people from bringing cafeteria food out here to feed the turtles. We think it's actually harming them," another team runs up shouting.

Team after team rushes to me with excitement and their plans for this large expedition and field project. I just take it all in. They have it; they have an Explorer's Mindset.

A scientist carries out a turtle tracking survey they created.

PUSHING BOUNDARIES WITH
AN EXPLORER'S MINDSET

This particular year, eager third-grade scientists completed a full-scale turtle tracking project. They organized a system to number and identify turtles and mapped their travel patterns and behavior each day with the use of nature journaling. They began creating public service announcements to educate the entire school (we are PK–12) about everything from the species of the turtles, the harm of feeding them "people food," and their plan to take care of them by tracking over time. They made careful observations, built a sense of responsibility in taking care of the area and communicating with the school community, and sought out possible problems the turtles would face in surviving and worked to solve them in collaborative teams. All of this was fueled by their own curiosity and my willingness to support their ideas and empower them to be explorers.

Thinking like an explorer, or the Explorer's Mindset, is made up of specific attitudes and skills, as outlined by the National Geographic Society and Education Team. Integrating this into my classroom was the direct result of investigating National Geographic's learning framework and my commitment to becoming a National Geographic Certified Educator back in 2016. Being exposed to this approach to learning and planning has forever changed my perspective and educational philosophy.

Before becoming a National Geographic Certified Educator, portions of the framework and Explorer's Mindset were already present within my approach; however, I became exponentially stronger as an educator as a result of deeper study of the framework and Explorer's Mindset in particular.

I know some of you gave a little eye roll as soon as you read "mindset" in this chapter's title. How many times will we hear this word?

Attitudes

I know, I know. I, too, feel that pain and struggle to keep my eyes forward when I hear the word. Do me a favor, can you hang with me for a moment and give it a chance?

Skills

The Explorer's Mindset is comprised of these attitudes and skills: Curiosity, Responsibility, Empowerment, Observation, Communication, Collaboration, and Problem-Solving. Scan the QR codes to see the attitudes and skills of an explorer during different developmental stages, ages, and grade levels of learners.

Basically, good teaching, right? This mindset can be used in any content area, but this book is specifically attacking science and how we can disrupt the norms, making science real and authentic, something that we have somehow lost along the way in the world of education.

The Explorer's Mindset invites you to think differently, plan differently, and take steps toward a more authentic investigation. In catering toward the natural *curiosity* about the world around us, we instantly engage learners in their environment, inviting their curiosity to take hold and drive our experience together. In using their curiosity to drive investigation, learners then become *empowered* as explorers and create a sense of *responsibility* for becoming stewards of their learning and the concepts at hand. In their investigations, they begin to *collaborate* and *communicate* in new ways within their own classroom community and the larger community around them. Through careful *observations*, they identify real and relevant *problems* to *solve* that require creative thinking. All of this cascades into beautiful learning opportunities and authentic immersion into the world around them through your content. The Explorer's Mindset is more than just another buzzword; it's a challenge, motivation, and inspiration to push ourselves further as professionals and our learners further as changemakers in the world around them.

Disrupting science education as we know it takes a different mentality, a desire to create meaningful and positive change, the drive to push forward no matter what noes obstacles, challenges, or eye rolls from colleagues you encounter. Science was meant to be experienced, to push boundaries, to provoke questions, and seek the answers. What you will find is that the answers end up actually being questions, questions that beg you to continue investigating, learning, and asking more questions. You must explore, and you must have the mindset of an explorer or educator explorer.

Are you ready? Are you prepared to be on this expedition together? Are you ready to be an explorer? Your learners are, so what are you waiting for?

I am an explorer. I am an educator explorer. This is your invitation to join my expedition team. Join me in the field, and let's build our mindset together. Let's disrupt science.

Teaching through Field and Expedition Science

Field and expedition science immerse our learners into the content and the standards they have to know rather than in "one and done" type exposures. Even in the most well-intentioned classroom, content tends to be something received, not something learners do and experience in real time. With science in particular, we have such an opportunity to be immersive with content.

Though I cannot take my elementary-aged scientists to the Amazon to complete fieldwork with me, I can replicate portions of that work in the experiences I create for my young scientists. Let's take a look at one example of what I was able to do with my first-grade class.

Armed with their science journals, pencils, iPads, curiosity, and a thirst for adventure, my students and I set out from the classroom to explore our campus with one simple goal: record all the insects we find. We set out on this mission before my students even know how to differentiate insects from other living things like spiders. It doesn't matter. That will come. What matters is that they are out there in the field completing authentic expeditions. My goal is to prepare them to be their own expedition principal investigator, allowing me to become just a member of their field team, but for this, their first expedition, I am the PI. They follow along like ducklings in the spring, or perhaps young kittens wandering off in all directions. Semantics.

At any rate, we begin by locating what they think are insects and collecting specimen photographs. I guide their discoveries with observations like, "Wow, I notice they all have six legs. I wonder if that means that in order to be an insect, you must have six legs." They learn on location and in the field, with an expedition goal guiding our work: locate all insects. We use the iNaturalist and Seek applications to identify scientific and common names of our specimen, and later, back in the laboratory, we create a field guide for our campus of all the insects we found.

Like all great science does, this initial field experience sparks many questions:

What insect is most common on our campus?
Where on campus has the most grasshoppers?
What time of day are insects most active?
How can we protect insects on campus?
How many different types of bees are in our garden area?

My scientists were empowered not only to complete field-work as a member of my expedition team but to ask questions and design their own expedition and field experiences to investigate further. In one class period, we gained enough data and formed enough questions to fill weeks, if not months or even the entire year. These scientists are six and seven years old. What will they do next year? Where will they be in terms of scientific investigation when they are sixteen?

Kelly Koller (@kellkoll, @Outdoor_SEL)
elementary teacher and National Geographic Explorer,
explorermindset.org

I was first introduced to National Geographic Education's learning framework while beginning the educator certification program through the organization. At the time, I was teaching all content areas in a multi-age environmental charter school, grades six through eight. Field studies and physically being outdoors as stewards was already a central piece of our school culture. As you can imagine with juggling all that curriculum and context, launching into the unknown was something you had to be comfortable with as a teacher at that school. Or, as I like to say, be comfortable with being uncomfortable. The fact is when you take students out for field studies or overnight camping, something unexpected will happen—like an explosion of gold glitter in a rustic cabin or a student-created campfire dinner that takes four hours to cook. As lead teacher, I guided the identification of traits, like curiosity and grit, that helped us provide social-emotional support for learning while continuing to build on the culture of our school. When I saw the learning framework, I immediately saw similarities; however, I also saw that, with a K–12 continuum of competencies for attitudes and skills, it was much more thorough than what we had put together. I was hooked. While I had previously framed learning as an adventure, I also loved using exploration instead. My mindset shifted, and it has been there, passionately, ever since.

Even as I made a family-driven choice to go back to a traditional school that was close to our home because of the two-hour commute to the charter school, the Explorer Mindset stayed with me. As a sixth-grade English and social studies teacher, I coordinated field experiences for our grade level, like designing and planting a pollinator garden, using our school forest to teach mapping skills, and taking students outdoors for writing. At the time, I was also fortunate to be selected for the 2018 Grosvenor Fellowship, and my expedition was a twenty-four-day journey to the High Arctic of Canada and Greenland. With the extremes of a light, foggy notion of wanting to use the Explorer Mindset more, a bold openness to absorb, and a passion to adapt and create, I started the expedition with an internal challenge to let it transform me. Using my phone as a tool for collecting and curating, I took photos and videos of receding glaciers, icebergs, and amazing wildlife (polar bears, musk oxen, walruses, whales). But I also used my phone to interview people. Amazing people. I asked them about education. What helped them as learners? How did they think like an explorer in their personal or professional lives? Did it help them? Inspired and armed with an iMovie app, I put together YouTube videos for my students on the Explorer Mindset.

A month after I returned from the Arctic, I gave a TEDx talk titled "Learning with an Explorer Mindset." A month after that, I received news that I had been awarded a National Geographic Society grant to design an Explorer Mindset web tool, an online platform that coaches students through the process of reflecting on and developing their own Explorer Mindset. For me, my Arctic expedition revealed to me that the Explorer Mindset and content go hand in hand and that framing any content area with an Explorer Mindset means breathing life into it and changing the perspective. Content is not inflicted on you; you are an explorer of it. These are just a few strategies that I feel help flip that script and provide framing and opportunity for student-driven exploration.

I have really enjoyed using simple wording changes to change the perspective on daily learning targets. I started doing this while teaching a standards-driven, top-down English Language Arts curriculum, an expectation set by my district at the time. I discovered by simply changing my wording from things like "I can identify text features in nonfiction text" to "I can explore nonfiction text to discover text features" helps change the perspective on what we are doing and helps me provide a more student-centered way to present directed curriculum. Words are powerful, and this is an easy way to build an Explorer Mindset into the classroom culture of any content area.

I love the concept that we can use conversation to explore the world. Just like reading a book is a way to experience places and events that go beyond our own life, conversation can be used to explore and learn from others. Socratic seminar, a formal discussion based on a text, is a great method that can be used for students to explore an issue or question and practice valuable communication skills. A question is posed, a resource text or texts are provided, and learners are given time to read the text, determine their viewpoint on the question, and find evidence in the text that supports their position on the question. For discussion, I have students form circles in small groups where they listen closely to the comments of others, think critically for themselves, pose additional questions to the group, and share their thoughts, making sure to cite evidence that supports their opinion.

I am passionate about taking learners outside, period. For anything. Any schoolyard or outdoor setting, whether it is urban or rural, is rich with more detail than the four walls of a classroom can provide. It is also dynamic and changing, providing challenge, interest, and unlimited possibilities. One activity I love to do has students practice writing in detail by making observations and using sensory words. A word list of action verbs and words broken down by the senses "touch, sight, smell, hearing, taste" is helpful to provide to students to encourage detail and build vocabulary/literacy skills. Another activity I like to do pairs curiosity with observation. This activity was first introduced to me by another Grosvenor Fellow, Christine McCartney. Students find an object outdoors that piques their interest. They describe it, then pose a question about it on a piece of paper. Next, they place the object on or next to the paper and in a gallery style, students walk around and add follow-up questions or other observations on each other's papers. This is a great activity that can be done over and over again that helps build the Explorer Mindset culture into the classroom.

We were meant to explore this earth like children do, unhin-
dered by fear, propelled by curiosity and a sense of discovery.
Allow yourself to see the world through new eyes and know
there are amazing adventures here for you.

—Laurel Bleadon Maffei

When students imagine themselves as explorers, learning becomes
more exciting, personal, and meaningful. And when teachers imagine
themselves as explorers, they feel creative, empowered, and engaged,
too. Even though the Explorer Mindset has been such a central part of
my teaching practice, it is still a work in progress for me. I think it will
always be. After all, that is the nature of exploration. With an Explorer
Mindset, we are never finished; we just keep going #further.

CHAPTER SIXTEEN

CLOSING THOUGHTS

You don't have to be me.

In fact, I don't want you to be. I want you to be you.

This is an expedition, a journey to disrupt, improve, and elevate science education. I want you to be able to take something, anything, from this book and make it your own if you want. If you can do exactly what I do and it's what is best for your learners, go for it! If you can take a small portion of an idea and use it with your learners, awesome! Maybe something has sparked an idea, maybe it has caused you to reflect on your practices, affirm your amazing work, or show you something that can help strengthen your practice whether small or large; that's what it's about. I want this book to show you that you *can* do things differently, not highlight what you *can't*. The bottom line is we can and we must do better for our learners in the world of science. If you need a thought partner, a hype woman, a friend, or someone to message or tweet to, I am here. Please reach out, please message, and please follow (I will follow you back. Hold me to it!). This is your journey now. It started the moment you chose this book as something to read. I've taken you with me on my expedition; we're teammates now, and it's your turn to lead. Where will your expedition take *you*?

We will change the world through education; the first step is committing to it. By reading this book, I see you, you changemaker, you disrupter, you amazing educator. Let's disrupt science education together.

> ## Resources Mentioned in the Book:
>
> Books
> - *EDrenaline Rush* by John Meehan
> - *Instant Relevance* by Denis Sheeran
> - *Unpack Your Impact* by Naomi O'Brien and LaNesha Tabb
> - *Teach Your Class Off* by CJ Reynolds
>
> Twitter
> - #scitlap chat (every Wednesday at 8:30 p.m. Eastern)
> - #EducatorExplorer chat (first Sunday of each month at 8 p.m. Eastern)
>
> Must-Follow Hashtags and Handles for Diversity
> - #blackbirdersweek
> - @500queersci
> - @millionstem
> - @BlackAFinSTEM
> - @JedidahIslerPhD
> - @hood_naturalist
> - @ravenscimaven
> - @IndigenousTweets
> - @TerriHansen
>
> Website Resources
> - Explorer Mindset: explorermindset.org
> - Indigenous Land Claims: native-land.ca
> - BioBlitz: nationalgeographic.org/projects/bioblitz
> - SciStarter: scistarter.org
> - Explore by the Seat of Your Pants: exploringbytheseat.com
> - Explorer Classroom: nationalgeographic.org/education/student-experiences/explorer-classroom

- Skype a Scientist: skypeascientist.com
- National Parks: nps.gov/teachers/index.htm
- National Geographic: nationalgeographic.org/education/ classroom-resources

Apps
- iNaturalist
- Seek by iNauralist

Diverse Science Literature:

All Ages
- *Types of Scientists: A Coloring Book for All Ages* by Dr. Semarhy Quiñones-Soto

Younger Scientists
- *Cece Loves Science* by Kimberly Derting, Shelli R. Johannes, illustrated by Vashti Harrison
- *Sasha Savvy Learns to Code* by Stacia Deutsch and Reshma Saujani
- *Women Who Dared* by Linda Skeers and Livi Gosling
- *Talkin' about Bessie: The Story of Aviator Elizabeth Coleman* by Nikki Grimes, illustrated by E. B. Lewis
- *When the Shadbush Blooms* by Carla Messinger, Susan Katz, illustrated by David Fadden
- *Doc Like Mommy* by Dr. Crystal Bowe
- *Look What Brown Can Do* by T. Marie Harris, illustrated by Neda Ivanova
- *Shark Lady: The True Story of How Eugenie Clark Became the Ocean's Most Fearless Scientist* by Jess Keating, illustrated by Marta Álvarez Miguéns
- *Women in Science: 50 Fearless Pioneers Who Changed the World* by Rachel Ignotofsky
- *Whoosh! Lonnie Johnson's Super Soaking Stream of Inventions* by Chris Barton, illustrated by Don Tate

- *Wangari Maathai* by Franck Prevot, illustrated by Aurélia Fronty
- *She Sang Promise: The Story of Betty Mae Jumper, Seminole Tribal Leader* by J. G. Annino, illustrated by Lisa Desimini

Middle Years Scientists

- *The Toothpaste Millionaire* by Jean Merrill
- *May Chinn: The Best Medicine* by Ellen Butts and Joyce Schwartz
- *Girls Who Code* by Reshma Saujani
- *The Boy Who Harnessed the Wind* by William Kamkwamba and Bryan Mealer
- *Ada Byron Lovelace and the Thinking Machine* by Laurie Wallmark, illustrated by April Chu
- *Reaching for the Moon: The Autobiography of NASA Mathematician Katherine Johnson* by Katherine Johnson

Older Scientists

- *Braiding Sweetgrass: Indigenous Wisdom, Scientific Knowledge, and the Teachings of Plants* by Robin Wall Kimmerer
- *The Boiling River: Adventure and Discovery in the Amazon* by Andrés Ruzo
- *Broad Band: The Untold Story of the Women Who Made the Internet* by Claire L. Evans
- *Archaeology from Space: How the Future Shapes Our Past* by Sarah Parcak
- *An Indigenous Peoples' History of the United States* by Roxanne Dunbar-Ortiz

Virtual and Augmented Reality

- Virtuali-Tee
- Merge Cube
- CoSpaces

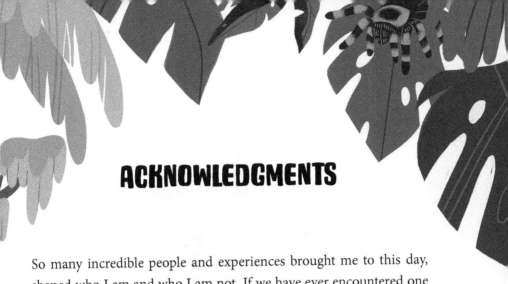

ACKNOWLEDGMENTS

So many incredible people and experiences brought me to this day, shaped who I am and who I am not. If we have ever encountered one another from anything between a simple smile, hello, or full-blown relationship, you are a part of me and I thank you from the bottom of my being. I often think about how I am literally a conglomeration of everyone I have ever met, stealing their positive attributes and making them a part of me. Who am I, really? But I digress.

There are a few I simply must acknowledge by name: Adam Welcome, Aleshia Dunning, Andrés Ruzo, Lori Nye, Dr. Shamaine Williams, the Virginia Association of Science Teachers, the Virginia Geographic Alliance, National Geographic Society, Lindblad Expeditions, Longwood University, my #scitlap family, and every single one of my contributing authors. Without your experiences, insight, and support, I would not have been able to piece this book together. Each one of you pushes me to be my best, be true to who I am, and continue even when I am certain I cannot possibly continue. Thank you.

To my husband, Michael, and two children, Gabi and Luke, who deal with my crazy ideas, allow me to be creative, sometimes shut myself off from everything to be creative, and leave them for periods of time to be on expeditions around the world, thank you.

Finally, my father, Stan Winner, who passed on September 13, 2020. You, sir, I owe so much to, from the way I write, teach, and approach the outdoors with curiosity to my stubbornness and ability to accept nothing less than exceptional and near perfection. I am your daughter and I will never forget how you have made me half of the person I am today.

ABOUT THE AUTHOR

BECKY SCHNEKSER is an Educator Explorer, National Geographic Grantee and Certified Educator, Grosvenor Teacher Fellow, LEGO Master Educator, field scientist, mother, wife, environmentalist, and equity advocate from the ancestral lands of the Chesapeake, Lumbee, and Nanesmond tribes. When she's not teaching K-5 scientists mostly outdoors, you can find her in the field, usually the Peruvian Amazon; climbing trees in her own yard with her family; or crawling on the ground trying to get epic footage of nature to use with her scientists at school. She is an international speaker, professional development leader, and coach. She is available for coaching, mentoring, keynote addresses, breakout sessions, and book clubs. She loves connecting and learning, so feel free to reach out!

 expeditionschnekser.com

expeditionschnekser@gmail.com

@schnekser

PROFESSIONAL DEVELOPMENT AND KEYNOTE TOPICS

Becky's presentations and keynote topics can be tailored to your specific event. Here are a few keynotes and presentations she has delivered in the past:

- **Expedition Science: Empowering Learners through Exploration:** Transforming science instruction by making it authentic, hands-on, and exploratory in nature, connecting with living professionals, and allowing young scientists voice and choice in how and what they investigate.
- **Field and Expedition Science:** Engaging in field studies as a member of a team of professionals, a member of a team with your students, or both is transformative for you as an educator, professional, and lead learner with your young scientists—so how do you do it?
- **Teaching Is a Superpower:** We have the opportunity every single day to impact countless lives. Whether it's positive or negative is completely up to us. Let's discover how to harness that power and make our impact positive, always—igniting rather than extinguishing passions of students.
- **Teaching Outdoors:** Whether you want a change of scenery for students or to jump into exclusively teaching outdoors, let's talk about getting outdoors and/or bringing the outdoors in!
- **The Power of Storytelling:** Whether you want to hear her own stories from the field, discoveries, triumphs, lessons learned, or how to use storytelling in your classroom (or maybe both!), explore together how storytelling can transform your teaching.

- **Place-Based Education:** Use the power of place, Indigenous knowledge, land claims, history, and culture to immerse yourself and learners into your space.

Specifically for Younger Audiences:

- **Finding Your Passion:** My passion was crushed in third grade. After twenty-five years, I found it again and have vowed to relentlessly pursue it every day since, and you can, too!
- **Making a Difference:** Age doesn't matter when it comes to making a difference. Start today.

MORE FROM

Dave Burgess Consulting, Inc.

Since 2012, DBCI has been publishing books that inspire and equip educators to be their best. For more information on our titles or to purchase bulk orders for your school, district, or book study, visit **DaveBurgessConsulting.com/DBCIbooks**.

More from the Like a PIRATE™ Series

Teach Like a PIRATE by Dave Burgess
eXPlore Like a PIRATE by Michael Matera
Learn Like a PIRATE by Paul Solarz
Play Like a PIRATE by Quinn Rollins
Run Like a PIRATE by Adam Welcome
Tech Like a PIRATE by Matt Miller

Lead Like a PIRATE™ Series

Lead Like a PIRATE by Shelley Burgess and Beth Houf
Balance Like a PIRATE by Jessica Cabeen, Jessica Johnson, and Sarah Johnson
Lead beyond Your Title by Nili Bartley
Lead with Appreciation by Amber Teamann and Melinda Miller
Lead with Culture by Jay Billy
Lead with Instructional Rounds by Vicki Wilson
Lead with Literacy by Mandy Ellis

Leadership & School Culture

Culturize by Jimmy Casas
Escaping the School Leader's Dunk Tank by Rebecca Coda and Rick Jetter
Fight Song by Kim Bearden

From Teacher to Leader by Starr Sackstein

If the Dance Floor Is Empty, Change the Song by Joe Clark

The Innovator's Mindset by George Couros

It's OK to Say "They" by Christy Whittlesey

Kids Deserve It! by Todd Nesloney and Adam Welcome

Let Them Speak by Rebecca Coda and Rick Jetter

The Limitless School by Abe Hege and Adam Dovico

Live Your Excellence by Jimmy Casas

Next-Level Teaching by Jonathan Alsheimer

The Pepper Effect by Sean Gaillard

Principaled by Kate Barker, Kourtney Ferrua, and Rachael George

The Principled Principal by Jeffrey Zoul and Anthony McConnell

Relentless by Hamish Brewer

The Secret Solution by Todd Whitaker, Sam Miller, and Ryan Donlan

Start. Right. Now. by Todd Whitaker, Jeffrey Zoul, and Jimmy Casas

Stop. Right. Now. by Jimmy Casas and Jeffrey Zoul

Teachers Deserve It by Rae Hughart and Adam Welcome

Teach Your Class Off by CJ Reynolds

They Call Me "Mr. De" by Frank DeAngelis

Thrive through the Five by Jill M. Siler

Unmapped Potential by Julie Hasson and Missy Lennard

When Kids Lead by Todd Nesloney and Adam Dovico

Word Shift by Joy Kirr

Your School Rocks by Ryan McLane and Eric Lowe

Technology & Tools

50 Things You Can Do with Google Classroom by Alice Keeler and Libbi Miller

50 Things to Go Further with Google Classroom by Alice Keeler and Libbi Miller

140 Twitter Tips for Educators by Brad Currie, Billy Krakower, and Scott Rocco

Block Breaker by Brian Aspinall

Building Blocks for Tiny Techies by Jamila "Mia" Leonard

Code Breaker by Brian Aspinall

The Complete EdTech Coach by Katherine Goyette and Adam Juarez

Control Alt Achieve by Eric Curts

The Esports Education Playbook by Chris Aviles, Steve Isaacs, Christine Lion-Bailey, and Jesse Lubinsky

Google Apps for Littles by Christine Pinto and Alice Keeler

Master the Media by Julie Smith

Reality Bytes by Christine Lion-Bailey, Jesse Lubinsky, and Micah Shippee, PhD

Sail the 7 Cs with Microsoft Education by Becky Keene and Kathi Kersznowski

Shake Up Learning by Kasey Bell

Social LEADia by Jennifer Casa-Todd

Stepping Up to Google Classroom by Alice Keeler and Kimberly Mattina

Teaching Math with Google Apps by Alice Keeler and Diana Herrington

Teachingland by Amanda Fox and Mary Ellen Weeks

Teaching Methods & Materials

All 4s and 5s by Andrew Sharos

Boredom Busters by Katie Powell

The Classroom Chef by John Stevens and Matt Vaudrey

The Collaborative Classroom by Trevor Muir

Copyrighteous by Diana Gill

CREATE by Bethany J. Petty

Ditch That Homework by Matt Miller and Alice Keeler

Ditch That Textbook by Matt Miller

Don't Ditch That Tech by Matt Miller, Nate Ridgway, and Angelia Ridgway

EDrenaline Rush by John Meehan

Educated by Design by Michael Cohen, The Tech Rabbi

The EduProtocol Field Guide by Marlena Hebern and Jon Corippo

The EduProtocol Field Guide: Book 2 by Marlena Hebern and Jon Corippo

The EduProtocol Field Guide: Math Edition by Lisa Nowakowski and Jeremiah Ruesch

Game On? Brain On! by Lindsay Portnoy, PhD

Innovating Play by Jessica LaBar-Twomy and Christine Pinto

Instant Relevance by Denis Sheeran

LAUNCH by John Spencer and A.J. Juliani

Make Learning MAGICAL by Tisha Richmond

Pass the Baton by Kathryn Finch and Theresa Hoover

Project-Based Learning Anywhere by Lori Elliott

Pure Genius by Don Wettrick

The Revolution by Darren Ellwein and Derek McCoy

Shift This! by Joy Kirr

Skyrocket Your Teacher Coaching by Michael Cary Sonbert

Spark Learning by Ramsey Musallam

Sparks in the Dark by Travis Crowder and Todd Nesloney

Table Talk Math by John Stevens

Unpack Your Impact by Naomi O'Brien and LaNesha Tabb

The Wild Card by Hope and Wade King

The Writing on the Classroom Wall by Steve Wyborney

Inspiration, Professional Growth & Personal Development

Be REAL by Tara Martin

Be the One for Kids by Ryan Sheehy

The Coach ADVenture by Amy Illingworth

Creatively Productive by Lisa Johnson

Educational Eye Exam by Alicia Ray

The EduNinja Mindset by Jennifer Burdis

Empower Our Girls by Lynmara Colón and Adam Welcome

Finding Lifelines by Andrew Grieve and Andrew Sharos

The Four O'Clock Faculty by Rich Czyz

How Much Water Do We Have? by Pete and Kris Nunweiler

P Is for Pirate by Dave and Shelley Burgess

A Passion for Kindness by Tamara Letter

The Path to Serendipity by Allyson Apsey

Sanctuaries by Dan Tricarico

Saving Sycamore by Molly B. Hudgens

The SECRET SAUCE by Rich Czyz

Shattering the Perfect Teacher Myth by Aaron Hogan

Stories from Webb by Todd Nesloney

Talk to Me by Kim Bearden

Teach Better by Chad Ostrowski, Tiffany Ott, Rae Hughart, and Jeff Gargas

Teach Me, Teacher by Jacob Chastain

Teach, Play, Learn! by Adam Peterson

The Teachers of Oz by Herbie Raad and Nathan Lang-Raad

TeamMakers by Laura Robb and Evan Robb

Through the Lens of Serendipity by Allyson Apsey

The Zen Teacher by Dan Tricarico

Children's Books

Beyond Us by Aaron Polansky

Cannonball In by Tara Martin

Dolphins in Trees by Aaron Polansky

I Want to Be a Lot by Ashley Savage

The Princes of Serendip by Allyson Apsey

Ride with Emilio by Richard Nares

The Wild Card Kids by Hope and Wade King

Zom-Be a Design Thinker by Amanda Fox

CPSIA information can be obtained
at www.ICGtesting.com
Printed in the USA
FSHW021511030621
81978FS